SADLIER

VOCABULARY WORKSHOP®

ACHIEVE

Level D

Jerome Shostak

Senior Series Consultant

Vicki A. Jacobs, Ed.D.
Director, Teacher Education Program
Harvard Graduate School of Education
Cambridge, Massachusetts

Series Consultants

Louis P. De Angelo, Ed.D.
Superintendent of Schools
Diocese of Wilmington
Wilmington, Delaware

John Heath, Ph.D.
Professor of Classics
Santa Clara University
Santa Clara, California

**Sarah Ressler Wright,
 M.A. English Ed, NBCT**
Head Librarian
Rutherford B. Hayes High School
Delaware, Ohio

Carolyn E. Waters, J.D., Ed.S.
Georgia Dept. of Education (Ret.)
English Language Arts Consultant
Woodstock, Georgia

S® Sadlier

Reviewers

The publisher wishes to thank for their comments and suggestions the following teachers and administrators, who read portions of the series prior to publication.

Sr. Maureen Lawrence McDermott, IHM, PhD
Superintendent, Secondary Schools
Archdiocese of Philadelphia Schools
Philadelphia, PA

Aidan T. Brett
Teacher, Language Arts
Springfield High School
Springfield, PA

Kristy L. Raymond
English Teacher, Dept. Chair
Livermore High School
Livermore, CA

Audrey G. Silverman
National Board Certified English Teacher
Dr. Michael Krop Senior High School
Miami, FL

Dawn S. Wolfe
Teacher, English Department
Walnut Hills High School
Cincinnati, OH

Cover: Concept/Art and Design: MK Advertising, Studio Montage and William H. Sadlier, Inc. Cover pencil: Shutterstock.com/VikaSuh.
Photo Credits: age fotostock/Mary Evans Picture Library Ltd/Johan De Meester: 116; Topic Photo Agency: 81 *top right*; ZOONAR GMBH LBRF: 113 *left*. akg-images/Sputnik: 72. Alamy Stock Photo/24BY36: 188; ClassicStock: 104; Lee Dalton: 120; Nicholas Eveleigh: 164; foodfolio: 128; Manfred Grebler: 145 *bottom*; David R. Frazier Photolibrary, Inc.: 60; ihar leichonak: 204; Christiaan May: 212–213 *background*; moodboard: 64; North Wind Picture Archives: 172; Ville Palonen: 69 *right*; Gerry Reynolds: 25 *center*; Boaz Rottem: 145 *top*; SPUTNIK: 32; Dave Stamboulis: 56; Bettina Strenske: 108; Alexey Zarubin: 113 *left*. Animals Animals Earth Scenes/Roger De La Harpe: 69 *left*; Ardea/Mark Boulton: 144. Art Resource/The Jewish Museum, New York/Robert Mann Gallery: 125 *bottom right*; The Metropolitan Museum of Art/Robert Mann Gallery: 125 *top*. Artville: 56 *inset*, 57 *inset*. Associated Press/Jerome Delay: 157; Brandi Jade Thomas: 156 *left*; Susan Walsh: 148. Bridgeman Images/The Israel Museum/Jerusalem, Israel, Hats and Gloves, 1932 (b/w photo), Auerbach, Ellen (b. 1906) & Stern, Grete (1904–99): 125 *bottom left*; Look and Learn, Gulliver's Travel (gouache on paper), Quinto Nadir (1918–94)/Private Collection: 152; Philip Mould Ltd, London/Portrait bust of William Shakespeare (marble), Roubilac, Louis Francois (1695–1762) (follower of)/Private Collection: 160. Digital Vision/Michael Cleary: 112–113 *background*. Dreamstime.com/Raja Rc: 12–13 *center*. Geovision, Inc/Nils Fonstad: 124. Getty Images: 40; Bettmann: 24 *bottom*, 28, 36, 112 *bottom left*, 112 *bottom right*, 220; Greg Dale: 216; Natalie Fobes: 188 *background*; Jonathan And Angela: 57 *top*; Hein van den Heuvel: 189 *bottom*; Hulton Archive/Stringer: 16, 37; National Geographic/William A. Allard: 25 *top*; Popperfoto: 213 *left*; Science Source: 192; Juan Silva: 113 *right*; Sports Illustrated: 213 *right*; SuperStock: 208; Transcendental Graphics: 212 *right*; Visage: 88. The Granger Collection: 36–37 *background*, 80 *top left*, 81 *bottom right*, 84. The Image Works/Topham/ArenaPal: 113 *center*. Jean-Louis Klein & Marie-Luce Hubert: 176. iStockphoto.com/monkeybusinessimages: 10. Library of Congress, Prints & Photographs Division/Alexander Gardner/M.P.Rice: 44. New Mexico State Planning Office Photograph Collection, courtesy New Mexico State Records Center and Archives, image no. 11209: 24 *top*. Myrleen Pearson: 168 *bottom*, 169 *bottom*. Rob Van Petten: 132. Photodisc: 24 *bottom*, 25 *inset*, 156 *background*. Photolibrary/Imagesource: 57 *bottom*. Science Source/Mark Burnett: 189 *top*. Shutterstock.com/cofkocof: 168–169 *background*; Inu: 196; Login: 168 *top*; Melissa King: 212; Michael Melnikoff: 76; Antonio Jorge Nunes: 68–69 *background*; Leigh Prather: 12–13 *center*; Rex/Wing Nut/New Line/Saul Zaentz: 12–13 *background*, 12 *left*, 12 *center*, 12 *right*, 13 *right*; theromb: 124–125 *background*; Risto Viita: 24 *top*. Superstock/Gerald Lacz Images/Gerald Lacz: 68 *left*. Wikimedia/U.S. Department of State, Bureau of Public Affairs/National Archives and Records Administration, Records of the U.S. Information Agency, Record Group 306: 20.

Illustration Credits: Andrea Orani: 200–201; Sholto Walker: 100–101.

 and **Vocabulary Workshop®** are registered trademarks of William H. Sadlier, Inc.

Printed in the United States of America.
ISBN: 978-1-4217-8509-7
5 6 7 8 9 10 11 BRR 24 23 22 21 20

For additional online resources, go to SadlierConnect.com.

CONTENTS

iWords Audio Program is available at **SadlierConnect.com**.

PROGRAM FEATURES

For more than five decades, VOCABULARY WORKSHOP has proven to be a highly successful tool for vocabulary growth and the development of vocabulary skills. It has also been shown to help students prepare for standardized tests. VOCABULARY WORKSHOP ACHIEVE maintains that tradition in a newly designed format.

Each of VOCABULARY WORKSHOP ACHIEVE's 15 Units introduces 20 words in two 10-word lists—**Set A** and **Set B**. Both Set A and Set B contain exercises to help you develop deeper understanding of the 10 words in each set. Combined Sets A and B then provide practice with all 20 of the words in the Unit. Review and Word Study activities follow Units 3, 6, 9, 12, and 15 and offer practice with the 60 vocabulary words in the preceding three Units.

Each level of VOCABULARY WORKSHOP ACHIEVE introduces and provides practice with 300 vocabulary words and contains features such as reading passages, writing prompts, vocabulary in context, evidence-based questions, and word study that will help you to master these new vocabulary words and succeed in using skills to comprehend unfamiliar words.

Each Unit in VOCABULARY WORKSHOP ACHIEVE consists of the following sections for **Set A** and **Set B**: an introductory **Reading Passage** that shows how vocabulary words are used in context, **Definitions** that include sentences that give examples of how to use the words, **Using**

Context, Choosing the Right Word, and **Completing the Sentence**—activities that provide practice with the vocabulary words. Each introductory **Reading Passage** is a nonfiction text that includes most of the vocabulary words from the Unit to which it belongs. In addition, **Synonyms**, **Antonyms**, and **Vocabulary in Context** in combined Sets A and B round out each Unit with practice with all 20 Unit words.

The five Review sections cover all 60 words from their corresponding Units. **Vocabulary for Comprehension** is modeled on the reading sections of college entrance exams. It presents reading comprehension questions, including vocabulary-related items and evidence-based items that are based on the reading passages.

Word Study sections that contain activities on **Idioms**, **Denotation and Connotation**, and **Classical Roots** follow the Review. These sections will help you develop your understanding of figurative language and practice skills that will help you to determine the meaning of new and unfamiliar vocabulary.

The Final Mastery Test assesses a selection of words from the year and allows you to see the growth you have made in acquiring new vocabulary words and in mastering the comprehension skills you need to understand unfamiliar words.

ONLINE RESOURCES

SadlierConnect.com

Go to **SadlierConnect.com** to find iWords, an audio program that provides pronunciations, definitions, and examples of usage for all of the vocabulary words presented in this level of VOCABULARY WORKSHOP ACHIEVE. You can listen to the entire **Reading Passage** and the 20 Unit vocabulary words one word at a time, or download all of the words in any given Unit.

At **SadlierConnect.com** you will also find interactive vocabulary quizzes, flash cards, and interactive games and puzzles that will help reinforce and enrich your understanding of the vocabulary words in this level of VOCABULARY WORKSHOP ACHIEVE.

VOCABULARY IN CONTEXT

The context of a word is the printed text of which that word is part. By studying a word's context, we may find clues to its meaning. We might find a clue in the immediate or adjoining sentence or phrase in which the word appears; in the topic or subject matter of the passage; or in the physical features—such as photographs, illustrations, charts, graphs, captions, and headings—of a page itself.

The **Reading Passages** as well as the **Using Context, Choosing the Right Word, Vocabulary in Context**, and **Vocabulary for Comprehension** exercises that appear in the Units, the Reviews, and the Final Mastery Test provide practice in using context to decode and to determine the meaning of unfamiliar words.

Three types of context clues appear in the exercises in this book.

A **restatement clue** consists of a synonym for or a definition of the missing word. For example:

Faithfully reading a weekly newsmagazine not only broadens my knowledge of current events and world or national affairs but also _____ my vocabulary.

a. decreases   **b.** fragments   **c.** increases   **d.** contains

In this sentence, *broadens* is a synonym of the missing word, *increases*, and acts as a restatement clue for it.

A **contrast clue** consists of an antonym for or a phase that means the opposite of the missing word. For example:

"My view of the situation may be far too rosy," I admitted. "On the other hand, yours may be a bit (**optimistic, bleak**)."

In this sentence, *rosy* is an antonym of the missing word, *bleak*. This is confirmed by the presence of the phrase *on the other hand*, which indicates that the answer must be the opposite of *rosy*.

An **inference clue** implies but does not directly state the meaning of the missing word or words. For example:

"A treat for all ages," the review read, "this wonderful novel combines the _____ of a scholar with the skill and artistry of an expert _____."

a. ignorance . . . painter   **c.** wealth . . . surgeon

b. wisdom . . . beginner   **d.** knowledge . . . storyteller

In this sentence, there are several inference clues: (a) the word *scholar* suggests knowledge; (b) the words *novel*, *artistry*, and *skill* suggest the word *storyteller*. These words are inference clues because they suggest or imply, but do not directly state, the missing word or words.

VOCABULARY AND READING

There is a strong connection between vocabulary knowledge and reading comprehension. Although comprehension is much more than recognizing words and knowing their meanings, comprehension is nearly impossible if you do not know an adequate number of words in the text you are reading or have the vocabulary skills to figure out their meaning.

The **Reading Passages** in this level provide extra practice with vocabulary words. Vocabulary words are in boldface to draw your attention to their uses and contexts. Context clues embedded in the passages encourage you to figure out the meanings of words before you read the definitions provided on the pages directly following the passages.

Test Prep

Your knowledge of word meanings and your ability to think carefully about what you read will help you succeed in school and on standardized tests, including the SAT® and ACT® exams.

The **Vocabulary for Comprehension** exercises in each Review consist of a reading passage followed by comprehension questions. The passages and questions are similar to those that you are likely to find on standardized tests.

Types of Questions

You are likely to encounter the following types of questions in VOCABULARY WORKSHOP ACHIEVE and on standardized tests.

Main Idea Questions generally ask what the passage as a whole is about. Often, but not always, the main idea is stated in the first paragraph of the passage. You may also be asked the main idea of a specific paragraph. Questions about the main idea may begin like this:

- The primary or main purpose of the passage is . . .

- The author's primary or main purpose in the passage is to . . .

- Which of the following statements most nearly paraphrases the author's main idea in the ninth paragraph (lines 77–88)?

- The main purpose of the fourth paragraph (lines 16–25) is to . . .

Detail Questions focus on important information that is explicitly stated in the passage. Often, however, the correct answer choices do not use the exact language of the passage. They are instead restatements, or paraphrases, of the text.

Vocabulary in Context Questions check your ability to use context to identify a word's meaning. For example:

- As it is used in paragraph 2, "adherents" most nearly means . . .

Use the word's context in a passage to select the best answer, particularly when the vocabulary word has more than one meaning. The answer choices may contain two (or more) correct meanings of the word in question. Choose the meaning that best fits the context.

Inference Questions ask you to make inferences or draw conclusions from the passage. These questions often begin like this:

- It can be most reasonably inferred from the information in the fifth paragraph (lines 53–69) that . . .
- The passage clearly implies that . . .

The inferences you make and the conclusions you draw must be based on the information in the passage. Using the facts you learn from the passage in addition to the knowledge and reasoning you already have helps you understand what is implied and reach conclusions that are logical.

Evidence-Based Questions ask you to provide evidence from the passage that will support the answer you provided to a previous question. These questions often begin like this:

- Which choice provides the best evidence for the answer to the previous question?
- Which statement is the best evidence for the answer to the previous question?

Questions About Tone show your understanding of the author's attitude toward the topic of the passage. To determine the tone, pay attention to the author's word choice. The author's attitude may be positive (respectful), negative (scornful), or neutral (distant). These are typical questions:

- The author's primary purpose in the passage is to . . .
- Which word best describes the author's tone?

Questions About Author's Technique focus on the way a text is organized and the language the author uses. These questions ask you to think about structure and function. For example:

- In the context of the passage, the primary function of the fourth paragraph (lines 30–37) is to . . .
- The organizational structure of the passage is best described as . . .

To answer the questions, you must demonstrate an understanding of the way the author presents information and develops ideas.

VOCABULARY AND WRITING

The **Writing: Words in Action** prompt provides you with an opportunity to practice using text evidence to respond to a prompt about the introductory **Reading Passage**. You will have the opportunity to demonstrate your understanding of the Unit words by incorporating the new vocabulary you have learned into your own writing.

WORD STUDY

Word Study helps build word knowledge with strategies to help you look closely at words for meanings. Word Study instruction and practice include **Idioms**, **Denotation and Connotation**, and **Classical Roots**.

Idioms

Three Word Study sections feature instruction on and practice with idioms. An idiom is an informal expression whose literal meaning does not help the reader or listener understand what the expression means, such as "raining cats and dogs," "the apple of my eye," or "a dark horse." While every language has its own idioms, English is particularly rich in idioms and idiomatic expressions. Developing a clear understanding of idioms will help you better understand the figurative language that authors use in their writing.

Denotation and Connotation

Instruction in **Denotation and Connotation** and practice with connotations is included in two of the Word Study sections. Understanding a word's connotation will develop your skills as a reader, writer, and speaker.

Understanding the difference between denotation and connotation is important to understanding definitions and how concepts are used, as well as in choosing the right word. In these exercises, practice choosing the correct word by determining the emotional association of the word.

Classical Roots

Each Word Study includes a **Classical Roots** exercise that provides instruction in and practice with Greek and Latin roots. Developing a useful, transferable technique to make sense out of unfamiliar words through Greek and Latin roots will help you unlock the meanings of thousands of words. An example word drawn from the vocabulary words in the previous Units is referenced at the top of the page and serves as a guide to help you complete the exercise.

PRONUNCIATION KEY

The pronunciation is indicated for every basic word in this book. The pronunciation symbols used are similar to those used in most recent standard dictionaries. The author has primarily consulted *Webster's Third New International Dictionary* and *The Random House Dictionary of the English Language* (*Unabridged*). Many English words have multiple accepted pronunciations. The author has given one pronunciation when such words occur in this book except when the pronunciation changes according to the part of speech. For example, the verb *project* is pronounced **prə jekt'**, and the noun form is pronounced **präj' ekt**.

Vowels							
	ā	lake	e	stress	ü	loot, new
	a	mat	ī	knife	u̇	foot, pull
	â	care	i	sit	ə	jump, broken
	ä	bark, bottle	ō	flow	ər	bird, better
	au̇	doubt	ô	all, cord		
	ē	beat, wordy	oi	oil		

Consonants							
	ch	child, lecture	s	cellar	wh	what
	g	give	sh	shun	y	yearn
	j	gentle, bridge	th	thank	z	is
	ŋ	sing	th̶	those	zh	measure

All other consonants are sounded as in the alphabet.

Stress	The accent mark follows the syllable receiving the major stress: en rich'.

Abbreviations							
	adj.	adjective	*n.*	noun	*prep.*	preposition
	adv.	adverb	*part.*	participle	*v.*	verb
	int.	interjection	*pl.*	plural		

*Read the following passage, taking note of the **boldface** words and their contexts. These words are among those you will be studying in Unit 1. It may help you to complete the exercises in this Unit if you refer to the way the words are used below.*

I'll Wait for the Movie
<Compare-and-Contrast Essay>

Cue scene: Middle-Earth characters Aragorn, Legolas, and Gimli leap off a ship, swords in hand, to **breach** archenemy Sauron's lines in the epic Battle of Pelennor Fields. This is a crucial moment in the movie version of *The Lord of the Rings: Return of the King*. Alas, the haunting showdown with the ghostly **brigands** does not actually occur in author J.R.R. Tolkien's books.

Film fans do not have to speak Elvish to enjoy director Peter Jackson's blockbuster *Lord of the Rings* (LOTR) trilogy. But do the movies do justice to Tolkien's enduring and popular novels? And is it possible for the LOTR purist to watch the films without cringing at every discrepancy? Readers are often disappointed with movie adaptations of their favorite novels. In fact, they might be **predisposed** to dislike any movie version. This is a **perennial** problem for film directors, scriptwriters, readers, and moviegoers alike.

Filmmakers often **commandeer** the story and make it their own. Their motivation might be this cliché: "a picture paints a thousand words." They eliminate characters or events, or they add new ones. And authors can't complain: When they sell the rights to their work, they usually **relinquish** control. Filmmakers understand that their audience is **opinionated**, as evinced by LOTR fans posting online comments about Jackson's adaptation. Some claim that Jackson made a **muddle** of the books, that his tinkering is **spurious**, or that the films show only **spasmodic** flashes of greatness. Other fans show **unbridled** enthusiasm, saying that Tolkien's **perennial** classics are too long and **diffuse** and that

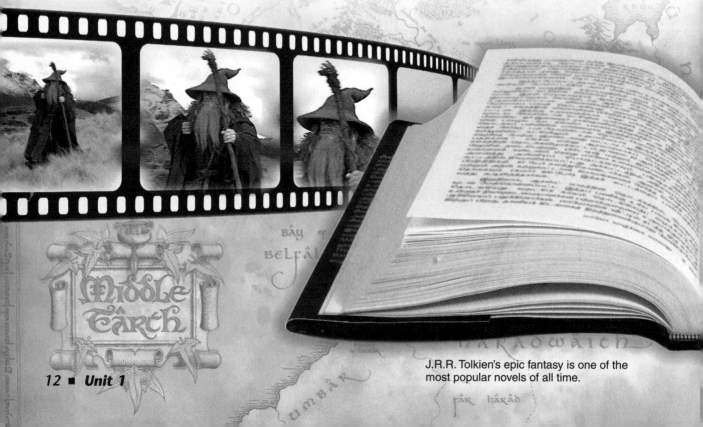

J.R.R. Tolkien's epic fantasy is one of the most popular novels of all time.

the director's snipping was essential. And some fans are more **circumspect** in their criticism, realizing it is impossible to please everyone.

The **dilemma** facing filmmakers is that reading a book is a more interactive experience than watching a movie. A reader visualizes every scene in the book and decides what the characters look and sound like, what they wear, how their environs appear. For those who read the LOTR books first, the movie's Frodo may not resemble the Frodo they imagined. How can Peter Jackson's vision of Middle-Earth reflect the ones created in the mind's eye of millions of readers?

It is easy to imagine that moviegoers and readers are always **deadlocked** over which medium is better. Those who have read the book may come away from the multiplex disappointed: *The movie left out so much! Why was that memorable scene transposed to the beginning?* On the other hand, those who see the movie first may be awed by the director's imaginative retelling or by the stirring music and special effects. Most movies based on books retain key characters, scenes, and themes. Directors and scriptwriters strive to tell the same story and evoke the same emotions as the author of the original book. Both share an audience yet address one that is exclusively their own.

In the end, directors must rely on fans to accept the limitations of the movie. How is it possible for a two-hour movie (or even a sprawling movie trilogy) to include all of the details woven throughout a long novel? A movie that attempted to do this would end up unwieldy and **cumbersome**—a surefire way to disappoint moviegoers and book lovers alike.

Audio

For iWords and audio passages, go to SadlierConnect.com.

A poster for the first movie in director Peter Jackson's *Lord of the Rings* trilogy.

Definitions

Note the spelling, pronunciation, part(s) of speech, and definition(s) of each of the following words. Then write the appropriate form of the word in the blank space in the illustrative sentence(s) following.

1. admonish
(ad män' ish)

(*v.*) to caution or advise against something; to scold mildly; to remind of a duty

The librarian had to _____ the noisy students several times before they settled down.

2. brigand
(brig' ənd)

(*n.*) a bandit, robber, outlaw, highwayman

Ancient caravans passing through desolate areas were sometimes attacked by _____.

3. commandeer
(käm ən dēr')

(*v.*) to seize for military or official use

Under certain circumstances the U.S. government has the right to _____ private property.

4. cumbersome
(kəm' bər səm)

(*adj.*) clumsy, hard to handle; slow-moving

The bus was filled to capacity with holiday shoppers carrying large and _____ packages.

5. diffuse
(*v.*, dif yüz';
adj., dif yüs')

(*v.*) to spread or scatter freely or widely; (*adj.*) wordy, long-winded, or unfocused; scattered or widely spread

The scent of lilacs slowly _____ through the open window.

The speech was so long and _____ that most audience members were thoroughly confused by it.

6. dilemma
(di lem' ə)

(*n.*) a difficult or perplexing situation or problem

During the crisis the President found himself caught in a painful _____.

7. muddle
(məd' əl)

(*v.*) to make a mess of; muddle through: to get by; (*n.*) a hopeless mess

Too much stress and too little sleep will almost certainly _____ a person's ability to concentrate.

The _____ was principally caused by their failure to carry out the general's orders properly.

8. predispose
(prē dis pōz')

(*v.*) to incline to beforehand

My genetic makeup seems to _____ me to colds and sore throats.

9. spurious
(spyü' rē əs)

(*adj.*) not genuine, not true, not valid

Manufacturers who make _____ claims for their products may face fines or lawsuits.

10. unbridled
(ən brīd' əld)

(*adj.*) lacking in restraint

Sometimes the _____ enthusiasm of sports fans can get a little out of hand.

Using Context

*For each item, determine whether the **boldface** word from pages 14–15 makes sense in the context of the sentence. Circle the item numbers next to the six sentences in which the words are used correctly.*

1. She was in such a somber mood that even the beautiful weather could not **predispose** her from moping.

2. According to legend, Robin Hood was a good-hearted **brigand** who robbed from the rich to give to the poor and less fortunate.

3. Compared to today's camping tents, which are lightweight and easy to assemble, those old tents are heavy and **cumbersome**.

4. Because of low enrollment, the parks and recreation department had to **admonish** the exercise class that had been scheduled for 10:30 a.m. on Tuesdays.

5. A good editor can help turn a long, **diffuse** explanation into a clear and concise one.

6. The judge was critical of the lawyer and reminded him that **spurious** lawsuits waste the court's time and the public's money.

7. When you are interested in taking several different language classes but have time for only one in your schedule, you face a **dilemma**.

8. This book describes history's greatest military leaders and the principles that they used to **commandeer** their troops.

9. The actors and director won praise for the **muddle** they had created by updating Shakespeare's *Romeo and Juliet* and setting it in present-day London.

10. My aunt's **unbridled** sense of curiosity about the natural world has led her to travel extensively.

Choosing the Right Word

*Select the **boldface** word that better completes each sentence. You might refer to the passage on pages 12–13 to see how most of these words are used in context. Note that the choices might be related forms of the Unit words.*

1. Like the rings a pebble makes when tossed in a pool of water, the good feelings generated by Dr. King's speech (**diffused, commandeered**) through the crowd.

2. The dean (**diffused, admonished**) the members of the team for neglecting their homework assignments.

3. The organization of some government agencies is so (**cumbersome, unbridled**) that it is all but impossible to know who is responsible for various activities.

4. In spite of weeks of practice, she made a (**dilemma, muddle**) of her performance.

5. Instead of trying to (**admonish, commandeer**) the support of the student body, we must earn it by showing our sincerity and ability.

6. Although he was the world's expert on the subject, his lectures were so (**spurious, diffuse**) that even his greatest fans grew bored.

7. The nation was faced with a (**dilemma, brigand**) in which either to advance or to retreat might endanger its vital interests.

8. Our city government seems to have (**predisposed, muddled**) into a first-rate financial crisis.

9. The robber barons were a group of nineteenth-century captains of industry who amassed wealth by means that a (**brigand, muddle**) might use.

10. The evidence intended to show that some races or nationalities are superior to others proved to be completely (**spurious, cumbersome**).

11. An economy in which the marketplace is considered "open" is one in which competition is more or less (**muddled, unbridled**).

12. How can you expect to succeed at your new job when you are (**diffused, predisposed**) to believe that it is "not right" for you?

Completing the Sentence

Choose the word from the word bank that best completes each of the following sentences. Write the correct word or form of the word in the space provided.

admonish	commandeer	diffuse	muddle	spurious
brigand	cumbersome	dilemma	predispose	unbridled

1. The idea of a(n) _____ like Robin Hood who helps the poor appeals strongly to the popular imagination.

2. The nurse rushed into the hospital corridor to _____ the visitors who were creating a disturbance.

3. To capture the fleeing criminals, the police _____ our car and raced after the vanishing truck.

4. The rug was rolled into such a(n) _____ bundle that it took four of us to carry it up the stairs.

5. The doctor became more and more fearful that her patient's weakened condition would _____ him to pneumonia.

6. Though all modern scholars accept *Macbeth* as Shakespeare's work, there continue to be _____ allegations that other writers wrote the play.

7. The records of our club were in such a(n) _____ that we couldn't even determine which members had paid their dues.

8. A man of towering pride and _____ ambition, he stopped at nothing to achieve his goals as quickly and directly as possible.

9. I have a(n) _____: If I don't get a job, I won't have the money to do what I want; and if I do get a job, I won't have the time.

10. I added a few drops of food coloring to the liquid and watched as they slowly _____ through it.

Definitions

Note the spelling, pronunciation, part(s) of speech, and definition(s) of each of the following words. Then write the appropriate form of the word in the blank space in the illustrative sentence(s) following.

1. **breach**
   (brēch)

   (*n.*) an opening, gap, rupture, rift; a violation or infraction; (*v.*) to create an opening, break through

   Because of a serious _____ of the rules, two players were ejected from the game.

   Our troops were unable to _____ the enemy's lines during the battle.

2. **circumspect**
   (sər' kəm spekt)

   (*adj.*) careful, cautious

   It is important for a diplomat to behave in a manner that is both discreet and _____.

3. **deadlock**
   (ded' läk)

   (*n.*) a standstill resulting from the opposition of two equal forces or factions; (*v.*) to bring to such a standstill

   After fifteen innings, the score remained a frustrating 3-to-3 _____.

   The refusal of labor and management to modify their demands _____ the contract negotiations.

4. **debris**
   (də brē')

   (*n.*) scattered fragments, wreckage

   After the storm, the beach was littered with driftwood and other _____.

5. **efface**
   (e fās')

   (*v.*) to wipe out; to keep oneself from being noticed

   Time had _____ almost all signs of the struggle that took place on that famous battlefield.

6. **opinionated**
   (ə pin' yən āt id)

   (*adj.*) stubborn and often unreasonable in holding to one's own ideas, having a closed mind

   My friend is so _____ that sometimes she will not listen to a reasonable proposal.

7. **perennial**
   (pə ren' ē əl)

   (*adj.*) lasting for a long time, persistent; (*n.*) a plant that lives for many years

   Pizza is a _____ favorite of young and old alike in the United States.

   A garden of _____ is relatively easy to maintain.

8. **relinquish**
(rē liṇ′ kwish)

(v.) to let go, give up

Severe illness forced me to _____ my role in the school play.

9. **salvage**
(sal′ vij)

(v.) to save from fire or shipwreck; (n.) property thus saved

Fortunately, we were able to _____ a few things from the fire.

_____ from sunken ships can be of great value to archaeologists and historians.

10. **spasmodic**
(spaz mäd′ ik)

(adj.) sudden and violent but brief; fitful; intermittent

_____ flashes of lightning and booming thunderclaps were accompanied by torrential rain.

Using Context

*For each item, determine whether the **boldface** word from pages 18–19 makes sense in the context of the sentence. Circle the item numbers next to the six sentences in which the words are used correctly.*

1. Some people think my father is overly **opinionated**, but I'm inspired by his passion for so many issues.

2. Although the two diplomats had been negotiating for hours, by the end of the day they remained in a frustrating **deadlock**.

3. The network decided to **salvage** the television show after a season of declining ratings.

4. The suitcase was so **circumspect** I could barely lift it off the ground.

5. Despite the hard work and many years of school required, she vowed she would never **relinquish** her goal of becoming a doctor.

6. After the storm, we went outside to assess the damage and begin cleaning up the **debris**.

7. The wind will **efface** the pollen so far and wide that all the cars will be covered in it.

8. All passwords were immediately reset because of the **breach** in the security of the company's network.

9. Watching the ball drop at midnight on New Year's Eve is a **perennial** tradition that began in 1907 at Times Square in New York City.

10. Because of the beautiful weather, we made a **spasmodic** decision to go to the beach.

Choosing the Right Word

*Select the **boldface** word that better completes each sentence. You might refer to the passage on pages 12–13 to see how most of these words are used in context. Note that the choices might be related forms of the Unit words.*

1. Rosa Parks became known as "the first lady of civil rights" after refusing to (**efface, relinquish**) her seat on a city bus so that a white passenger could sit there instead.

2. After the fire, investigators searched through the (**debris, breach**) for clues that might reveal the cause.

3. My mother broke the (**debris, deadlock**) in the quarrel between my brother and me by saying that neither of us could use the car.

4. His attempts to rid his administration of inefficiency were so (**circumspect, spasmodic**) that he came to be called the "reformer by fits and starts."

5. Even her refusal to dance with him did not seem to make a (**deadlock, breach**) in his gigantic conceit.

6. To ensure they are not resented, the most powerful nations in the world must be extremely (**circumspect, opinionated**) in their foreign policy.

7. When his precious collection of (**perennials, debris**) was torn up and trampled, the gardener was first heartbroken, then angry.

8. Since she is so convinced that there is only one right way—her way—I find her too (**spasmodic, opinionated**) for my liking.

9. After we agreed on the lineup of songs, we then (**salvaged, deadlocked**) over the choice of a name for our band.

10. If only I could (**breach, efface**) the memory of the look of shock and disappointment on my father's face!

11. Developing nations in all parts of the world face the (**perennial, circumspect**) problem of gaining a higher level of economic growth.

12. In general, she is a confident person, so I'm sure she will be able to (**relinquish, salvage**) a few shreds of self-respect from her humiliating failure.

Completing the Sentence

Choose the word from the word bank that best completes each of the following sentences. Write the correct word or form of the word in the space provided.

breach	deadlock	efface	perennial	salvage
circumspect	debris	opinionated	relinquish	spasmodic

1. Before I make an investment, I study all aspects of the situation in a methodical and _____ manner.

2. He is so _____ that he won't even consider the ideas or suggestions offered by other people.

3. Though my memory is getting dimmer and dimmer with the slow passage of time, I doubt that the exciting events of my childhood will ever be totally _____ from my mind.

4. Though his partner lost everything, he was able to _____ a few dollars from the wreckage of the bankrupt business.

5. An electronic malfunction caused the overhead crane on the assembly line to fling items from the conveyor belt in a wild and _____ manner.

6. The two sides in the lawsuit reached a(n) _____ when neither was willing to meet the other partway.

7. Many a teenager's room is strewn with clothing, sports equipment, and all sorts of _____.

8. Once Great Britain had given up her vast overseas empire, she found that she had also _____ her position as a world power.

9. The water pouring through the _____ in the dam threatened to flood the entire valley.

10. Since we do not want to replace the plants in our garden every year, we favor _____ over annuals.

Synonyms

*Choose the word or form of the word from this Unit that is the same or most nearly the same in meaning as the **boldface** word or expression in the phrase. Write that word on the line. Use a dictionary if necessary.*

1. an **uncontrolled** appetite for luxury   _____
2. a minor security **transgression**   _____
3. **warn** a child   _____
4. able to **rescue** cherished mementos   _____
5. the **jumble** of languages spoken   _____
6. a **rambling** and confusing letter   _____
7. too **inflexible** about her ideas   _____
8. frustrated by **awkward** procedures   _____
9. **make susceptible** to infection   _____
10. **taken over** by the troops   _____
11. cleared the **rubble**   _____
12. the **predicaments** of life   _____
13. **worn away** by erosion   _____
14. a **stalemate** in the peace talks   _____
15. captured by **thieves**   _____

Antonyms

*Choose the word or form of the word from this Unit that is most nearly opposite in meaning to the **boldface** word or expression in the phrase. Write that word on the line. Use a dictionary if necessary.*

1. **chronic** muscle contractions   _____
2. behave in a **reckless** manner   _____
3. delivered a **valid** argument   _____
4. made **infrequent** visits   _____
5. **retained** the title to the plot of land   _____

Writing: Words in Action

Do you prefer reading a book to seeing a movie, or do you think that movies tell a story in a more interesting way? In a brief essay, support your opinion with specific examples from your observations, studies, reading (refer to pages 12–13), or personal experience. Use three or more words from this Unit.

Vocabulary in Context

*Some of the words you have studied in this Unit appear in **boldface** type. Read the passage below, and then circle the letter of the correct answer for each word as it is used in context.*

In 2012, J.R.R. Tolkien's expansive imagination came to the big screen again, this time with the first film of *The Hobbit* trilogy. Middle-earth, the setting of *The Hobbit*, is full of wizards, hobbits, and elves. Production, costume, and make-up designers all brought Tolkien's vision to life. The filmmakers leave little cause for hard-core Tolkien fans to **admonish** them about deviations from the story. Filmed in New Zealand, the movie's production designers used physical and virtual sets to create mountains, tunnels, and bridges. Production designers were also tasked with turning an area in New Zealand's Southern Alps into Lake-town, the scene of an epic battle that ultimately ended with a fiery field of **debris** from which Middle-earth's inhabitants had to **salvage** their possessions.

Two other elements of creating a realistic setting are costume design and make-up design. To create wizards, hobbits, and elves, costume designers used multiple fabrics, textures, and colors to emphasize the differences between each type of character. Finally, make-up designers had to **efface** almost all human features to make their elves, hobbits, and wizards as true to Middle-earth as possible. They worked from hundreds of sketches to capitalize on the costumes and make each character distinct. Although some of the make-up was derived from 3D images, make-up artists also used large, **cumbersome** wigs made of yak hair for beards. These artists, along with all others who worked on the film trilogy, have themselves to thank for masterfully bringing J.R.R. Tolkien's **perennial** classic to life on the screen.

---

1. The word **admonish** most nearly means
   a. appreciate
   b. scold
   c. promote
   d. congratulate

2. A field of **debris** contains
   a. public records
   b. missing objects
   c. scattered fragments
   d. personal property

3. To **salvage** one's possessions means to
   a. save them from fire or wreckage
   b. keep them for oneself
   c. deliver them to an address
   d. sell them for a profit

4. To **efface** almost all human features, make-up designers had to
   a. keep them intact
   b. enhance them
   c. wipe them out
   d. duplicate them

5. A **cumbersome** wig is
   a. hard to handle
   b. sewn by machine
   c. easy to misplace
   d. difficult to make

6. *The Hobbit* is a **perennial** classic because it has
   a. outsold all other books
   b. inspired a movie
   c. been written for children
   d. lasted for a long time

Read the following passage, taking note of the **boldface** words and their contexts. These words are among those you will be studying in Unit 2. It may help you to complete the exercises in this Unit if you refer to the way the words are used below.

Cowgirl Up!
<Historical Nonfiction>

People today may consider cowgirls to be folk heroines, but many of the women who helped open America's western cattle country would have **jeered** and laughed at the term. It had a hint of the **dissolute** until well into the twentieth century. Cowgirls were associated with **comely** female sharpshooters, ropers, and trick riders of Wild West shows. At that time, working in entertainment meant **expulsion** from respectable society. But, it is said that you can't judge a horse by its color, and the West benefited from the work of all the women there.

Susan McSween

There was a precedent in the West for women ranchers in the areas governed by Spain from 1697 to 1848. Husbands and wives co-owned vast homesteads. Under Spanish law, wives could inherit property. Land ownership **fortified** the social status of women. Early generations of ranch women were **unflinching** and determined as they undertook all but the heaviest chores. They rode horses, herded cattle, and performed much of the work wealthy ranchers could **compensate** cowboys to do, and all the while, these women tended their homes and families. Their contributions helped turn struggling ranches into **lucrative** enterprises.

Some women of the old West are legends, while others have stories that have only been remembered by their families. Susan McSween lived in New Mexico at the time of Billy the Kid and the Lincoln County Wars. Rather than **adjourn** to a humdrum town life after her husband's murder in 1878, young Susan McSween purchased a ranch. Soon McSween, "The Cattle Queen of New Mexico," owned over 8,000 head of cattle. She lived much of her life running her ranch and selling real estate.

Lily Casey grew up in the early 1900s in a one-room house in West Texas, where, as a young child, she drove the family wagon to town to sell eggs. Her family bought a ranch in New Mexico when she was 11 years old. Casey's mother did not find the **alien**, difficult ranch work **tantalizing**, so Casey began overseeing most of the ranch work when she was barely a teenager. Exhausted by running the ranch without support, Casey left home at age 15 to teach in a town 500 miles away. She rode a horse all the

Calamity Jane

way and arrived at her new job, **sullied** and hungry, 28 days later. Casey taught for many years before returning to ranching during the 1930s.

Nobody would pin the label **mediocre** on the life of Martha Jane Canary. Born in 1852 in Missouri, she was separated from her family at an early age. To support herself, she worked **erratically** as a waitress, a nurse, a pony express rider, a mule- and ox-team driver, and a gold prospector. It was during her time as an army scout that she met Buffalo Bill and earned her famous nickname, "Calamity Jane." She traveled through much of the West, and stories of her adventures **proliferated**. She died in South Dakota in 1903. She is buried next to another western hero whose life is **fodder** for outrageous stories—Wild Bill Hickok.

While early ranch women were the first cowgirls, such women exist today. The National Cowgirl Hall of Fame in Texas first opened its doors in 1975 and has over 150 inductees. Among the cowgirls honored are a Pulitzer Prize winner, the first female chief of the Cherokee Nation, and a Supreme Court Justice.

Audio

For iWords and audio passages, go to SadlierConnect.com.

Definitions

Note the spelling, pronunciation, part(s) of speech, and definition(s) of each of the following words. Then write the appropriate form of the word in the blank space in the illustrative sentence(s) following.

1. alien
(ā′ lē ən)

(*n.*) a citizen of another country; (*adj.*) foreign, strange

Movies about _____ from outer space have been extremely popular for decades.

An _____ species of plant or animal can upset the balance of an ecosystem.

2. comely
(kəm′ lē)

(*adj.*) having a pleasing appearance

The proud parents and their _____ children posed for a family portrait.

3. erratic
(e rat′ ik)

(*adj.*) not regular or consistent; different from what is ordinarily expected; undependable

Students who have an _____ attendance record may find themselves disciplined by the principal.

4. fodder
(fäd′ ər)

(*n.*) food for horses or cattle; raw material for a designated purpose

Every experience in life is _____ for a novelist's imagination.

5. fortify
(fôr′ tə fī)

(*v.*) to strengthen, build up

The soldiers _____ the garrison against the expected attack.

6. jeer
(jēr)

(*v.*) to make fun of rudely or unkindly; (*n.*) a rude remark of derision

To _____ at someone with a disability is absolutely inexcusable.

Umpires and other referees quickly become immune to the _____ of angry fans.

7. mediocre
(mē dē ō′ kər)

(*adj.*) average, ordinary, undistinguished

The team's number-one draft pick turned out to be a rather _____ player, not a star who could lead them to the championship.

8. subjugate
(səb′ jü gāt)

(*v.*) to conquer by force, bring under complete control

"We must act quickly," the general said, "in order to _____ the rebel forces."

9. tantalize
(tan′ tə līz)

(*v.*) to tease, torment by teasing
When I am on a diet, the treats in bakery windows seem to have been put there to _____ me.

10. terse
(tərs)

(*adj.*) brief and to the point
The manuscript for my short story was returned to me with a _____ letter of rejection.

Using Context

*For each item, determine whether the **boldface** word from pages 26–27 makes sense in the context of the sentence. Circle the item numbers next to the six sentences in which the words are used correctly.*

1. According to the inspector's report, the longtime presence of termites and exposure to underground moisture would eventually **fortify** the building's foundation.

2. The weather at this time of year can be **erratic**—pleasant and mild one day, cold and stormy the next.

3. From her **terse** response to my message, I knew she had only a brief moment to check her email before boarding the train.

4. The armadillos here in Texas are **alien** to my cousin, who is from the Northeast and has never before seen creatures like these.

5. A good watchdog will alert its owners of danger by its **jeer** at intruders.

6. We could tell from the **comely** expression on our parents' faces that they were not amused by the twins' practical joke.

7. The accused criminal's refusal to answer questions added **fodder** to the investigators' suspicion that he had something to hide.

8. The fans rejoiced over the last-minute comeback of their team during the **mediocre** ending of the basketball game.

9. Despite weeks of fierce fighting, the king's forces were not able to **subjugate** the invaders and make them retreat.

10. The balloons, toys, and treats offered by the vendors at the street fair **tantalize** the child looking out from her window.

Choosing the Right Word

*Select the **boldface** word that better completes each sentence. You might refer to the passage on pages 24–25 to see how most of these words are used in context. Note that the choices might be related forms of the Unit words.*

1. Though a veteran soldier is often a well-tuned fighting machine, a raw recruit must be trained to avoid becoming cannon (**alien, fodder**).

2. His behavior is so (**erratic, terse**) that we never know what to expect from him.

3. The basketball team's uncharacteristic losing streak made the (**jeers, fodders**) echoing throughout the arena sting even more.

4. For centuries people have turned to the support of their friends and family to (**fortify, tantalize**) themselves against the shocks of daily life.

5. The usually captivating actress blamed her (**mediocre, terse**) stage performance on a lack of sleep.

6. I can understand how ordinary people sometimes feel (**tantalized, jeered**) by the wealth and luxuries they see displayed on television programs.

7. As soon as I entered that charming little cottage, I noticed that everything in it was neat and (**erratic, comely**).

8. The desire to force everyone to accept the same set of ideas is completely (**mediocre, alien**) to the spirit of democracy.

9. When I asked my mother why she wouldn't let me borrow the car, she (**comely, tersely**) explained that she needed it for herself.

10. We all experience fear and panic, but the leader of a great nation must be able to (**tantalize, subjugate**) such emotions.

11. The (**fodder, alien**), two-headed and covered with green scales, was grateful that the local people had welcomed him in spite of their misgivings.

12. All great athletes should know that the same fans who are cheering them today may be (**jeering, subjugating**) them tomorrow.

Completing the Sentence

Choose the word from the word bank that best completes each of the following sentences. Write the correct word or form of the word in the space provided.

alien	erratic	fortify	mediocre	tantalize
comely	fodder	jeer	subjugate	terse

1. A telegram was usually as _____ as possible, since there was a monetary charge for every word used in it.

2. Their only response to my warnings was to _____ at me scornfully and go ahead with their plans.

3. A(n) _____ student is one who neither fails any subject nor receives any marks that are above average.

4. Though he had a great sinker ball, he was so _____ on the mound that fans started to call him "Wild Pitch Hickok."

5. Our laws protect not only citizens but also _____ legally residing in this country.

6. Some people drink quantities of orange juice and swallow vitamin C tablets in a valiant attempt to _____ themselves against winter colds.

7. The farmer must provide storage facilities for the _____ he plans to set aside for his cattle during the long winter.

8. Though she is not a beautiful woman by conventional standards, she is certainly _____ and appealing.

9. To enlarge the areas under their control, kings of old sent out their armies to _____ their neighbors.

10. How can you be so cruel as to _____ those poor dogs by offering them tidbits that you will never let them have?

Definitions

Note the spelling, pronunciation, part(s) of speech, and definition(s) of each of the following words. Then write the appropriate form of the word in the blank space in the illustrative sentence(s) following.

1. adjourn
(ə jərn')

(v.) to stop proceedings temporarily; move to another place

The judge _____ the hearing until ten o'clock the following morning.

2. compensate
(käm' pən sāt)

(v.) to make up for; to repay for services

The manufacturer was ordered to _____ customers injured by the defective product.

3. dissolute
(dis' ə lüt)

(adj.) loose in one's morals or behavior

The mad Roman emperor Caligula led an extravagant and _____ life.

4. expulsion
(ek spəl' shən)

(n.) the process of driving or forcing out

The Biblical story of the _____ of Adam and Eve from the Garden of Eden is told in Genesis.

5. feint
(fānt)

(n.) a deliberately deceptive movement; a pretense; (v.) to make a deceptive movement; to make a pretense of

The chess master's opening _____ gave her an immediate advantage.

His uncanny ability to _____ and counterpunch made the champ unbeatable.

6. illegible
(i lej' ə bəl)

(adj.) difficult or impossible to read

The effects of air pollution have rendered the inscriptions on many old gravestones _____.

7. lucrative
(lü' krə tiv)

(adj.) bringing in money; profitable

Many people find that they can turn a favorite hobby into a highly _____ business.

8. proliferate
(prō lif' ə rāt)

(v.) to reproduce, increase, or spread rapidly

Because malignant cells _____, early detection of cancer is absolutely crucial to successful treatment.

9. sully
(səl′ ē)

(*v.*) to soil, stain, tarnish, defile, besmirch

The Nixon-era Watergate scandal _____ the image of politicians in the minds of many voters.

10. unflinching
(ən flin′ chiŋ)

(*adj.*) firm, showing no signs of fear, not drawing back

Everyone admires the _____ courage with which firefighters and other rescue workers carry out their dangerous jobs.

Using Context

*For each item, determine whether the **boldface** word from pages 30–31 makes sense in the context of the sentence. Circle the item numbers next to the six sentences in which the words are used correctly.*

1. The handwriting in the old letter was **illegible**, so I could barely make out the words.

2. Experts say that meditation is an effective way to **sully** your mind and ease anxious thoughts.

3. To **compensate** for my late arrival at my job this morning, I promised to work overtime.

4. None of us believed that my sister would make a living wage as a pet stylist, but she has had a surprisingly **lucrative** career.

5. As the earth's natural resources continue to **proliferate**, we must increase our conservation efforts.

6. The quarterback was warned that if his grades continued to decline, he would face the possibility of **expulsion** from the football team.

7. The politician who was originally considered the underdog impressed many during the debate by discrediting her opponent with **unflinching** confidence.

8. Shall we **adjourn** our conversation to the hallway so as not to disturb other patrons of the library?

9. The children were so well mannered and **dissolute** during the wedding ceremony that their parents praised their behavior.

10. The softball player's unintentional **feint** was a mistake that caused the team to lose the championship.

Choosing the Right Word

*Select the **boldface** word that better completes each sentence. You might refer to the passage on pages 24–25 to see how most of these words are used in context. Note that the choices might be related forms of the Unit words.*

1. Igor Stravinsky's opera *The Rake's Progress* paints a grim and uncompromising picture of some of the more (**dissolute, unflinching**) and degrading aspects of human behavior.

2. Over the years I've noticed one thing about rumors: Where the facts are few, fictions (**proliferate, feint**).

3. A best-selling book that is then made into a movie may be more (**dissolute, lucrative**) than the proverbial pot of gold at the end of the rainbow.

4. At one point in our fencing match, my opponent unexpectedly (**sullied, feinted**) to the left and threw me completely off guard.

5. When I first noticed how (**illegible, lucrative**) my roommate's handwriting was, I suggested that she sign up immediately for a course in penmanship.

6. The little girl wanted to see her brother flinch, so she made a sudden (**expulsion, feint**).

7. "No," he said, "I won't (**sully, adjourn**) your ears by repeating those mean and nasty rumors."

8. The detective was frustrated by the (**illegibility, expulsion**) of the letter, which made it difficult to determine who had written it.

9. To keep my self-respect, I must stand (**lucrative, unflinching**) before the authorities and tell them the truth as I see it.

10. After the formal dinner was over, we (**adjourned, proliferated**) to the den to continue our conversation in a more relaxed atmosphere.

11. I would be unwilling to vote for the (**expulsion, feint**) of club members just because they are behind in their dues.

12. Even though I must work hard for a living, I feel that the company I'm with amply (**adjourns, compensates**) me for my time and effort.

Completing the Sentence

Choose the word from the word bank that best completes each of the following sentences. Write the correct word or form of the word in the space provided.

| adjourn | dissolute | feint | lucrative | sully |
| compensate | expulsion | illegible | proliferate | unflinching |

1. The fact that you say you are truly sorry does not _____ for the pain I have suffered as a result of your cruelty.

2. The speaker advised us not to imitate the _____ kind of person who squanders time and money in the vain pursuit of pleasure.

3. He was a changed young man after his _____ from West Point for "conduct unbecoming an officer and a gentleman."

4. Despite all my efforts to make this a(n) _____ enterprise, it continues to be a decidedly unprofitable organization.

5. In spite of all the adverse criticism her ideas have received, she remains _____ in her determination to improve our community.

6. When it is time to end one of our meetings, a member must make a motion to _____.

7. Their so-called peace initiative proved to be nothing more than a clever _____ designed to lull the enemy into a false sense of security.

8. When the national economy is expanding, new housing developments begin to _____; when times are lean, construction slacks off.

9. The thoroughly disgraceful behavior of a few dissipated officers effectively _____ the honor of the entire unit.

10. Our doctor's handwriting is so _____ that my brother mistakenly used one of her prescriptions as a teacher's pass.

Synonyms

*Choose the word or form of the word from this Unit that is the same or most nearly the same in meaning as the **boldface** word or expression in the phrase. Write that word on the line. Use a dictionary if necessary.*

1. ordered the **ouster** of seven career diplomats _____
2. a candidate used to **taunts** by the crowd _____
3. an **attractive** group of youth _____
4. **bolstered** the milk with vitamins and minerals _____
5. **dodged** to the left and ran for a touchdown _____
6. found myself in **unfamiliar** territory _____
7. looked at her with a **steady** gaze _____
8. a **concise** answer _____
9. ordered to **reimburse** the victims of the swindle _____
10. **suspend** the discussion because of the late hour _____
11. a reputation for being **unpredictable** _____
12. **taint** his reputation _____
13. tried to **master** my hot temper _____
14. a supply of necessary **provisions** for our livestock _____
15. written in an **indecipherable** scrawl _____

Antonyms

*Choose the word or form of the word from this Unit that is most nearly opposite in meaning to the **boldface** word or expression in the phrase. Write that word on the line. Use a dictionary if necessary.*

1. a **virtuous** lifestyle _____
2. judged the work to be **exceptional** _____
3. weeds continue to **recede** in the garden _____
4. offered a **low** salary _____
5. **repulsed** by the sweet desserts _____

Writing: Words in Action

Write a short essay defining what a cowgirl is and the traits she embodies. Choose a woman from the passage and explain why she is the quintessential, or ideal, cowgirl. Use examples from your reading (refer to pages 24–25) and three or more words from this Unit to support your response.

Vocabulary in Context

*Some of the words you have studied in this Unit appear in **boldface** type. Read the passage below, and then circle the letter of the correct answer for each word as it is used in context.*

The roots of Hawaiian cowboy culture date back to the 1790s, when British explorer George Vancouver presented several head of Mexican longhorn cattle to Kamehameha, Hawaii's king. Vancouver also imparted some **terse** advice: prohibit killing the strange beasts for ten years. Hawaii's verdant landscape provided plenty of **fodder** for the king's new cattle, which soon multiplied into the thousands. To everyone's dismay, the wild cattle quickly became a public nuisance, wrecking farms, consuming thatched roofs, and scaring people. A second gift from the mainland would prove fortuitous. Hoping to gain favor with Kamehameha, an American merchant brought horses to the islands. These, too, bred, flourished, and grew wild.

By 1832, Kamehameha III had had enough of the cattle's destruction and sent an emissary to California to recruit Spanish-Mexican cowboys. The *vaqueros*' task was twofold—round up the wild cattle and teach Hawaiians how to be cowboys, or, as they would come to be known, paniolos (the Hawaiian pronunciation of *españoles*). Paniolos needed to learn horsemanship, beginning with how to **subjugate** and train Hawaii's mustangs. A paniolo and his horse had to be able to dodge and **feint** to move cattle where they did not want to go. In Hawaii, taking cattle to market involved a novel set of skills. Astride their horses, paniolos swam cattle through Hawaii's famous surf to waiting long boats, where the cattle, treading water, were tied off. Sailors then rowed the boats, with the cattle swimming alongside, out to ships, and the cattle were hoisted aboard.

Today, the future of Hawaii's cowboy is in doubt. The big cattle ranches, once **lucrative** enterprises, can no longer compete in global markets. As saddle shops and horse shoers have gone out of business, their now faded and **illegible** signs are remnants of a disappearing way of life.

---

1. Advice that is **terse** is
  a. dire   **c.** long-winded
  b. sensible   **d.** brief

2. Fodder for cattle is
  a. water   **c.** open space
  b. food   **d.** proper care

3. To **subjugate** a horse is to
  a. control it   **c.** feed it
  b. capture it   **d.** saddle it

4. To **feint** is to make a movement that is
  a. skilled   **c.** ambiguous
  b. difficult   **d.** deceptive

5. A **lucrative** business is
  a. competitive   **c.** large
  b. profitable   **d.** obsolete

6. The word **illegible** most nearly means
  a. broken down   **c.** unreadable
  b. incorrect   **d.** unimportant

*Read the following passage, taking note of the **boldface** words and their contexts. These words are among those you will be studying in Unit 3. It may help you to complete the exercises in this Unit if you refer to the way the words are used below.*

A Polar Controversy
<Historical Nonfiction>

Today, traveling by air greatly **abridges** the time it once took to reach the North Pole. In the first decade of the 20th century, before airplanes, reaching that remote, frozen destination was no easy task. Those who attempted it had to **surmount** hazardous conditions, such as **rifts** in thick, drifting sea ice and bitter winds that made breathing painful. Nonetheless, reaching the Pole first was an elusive prize that adventurers ardently sought. Then toward the end of that decade, two **eminent** American explorers, Frederick Cook and Robert E. Peary, friends and cotravelers, each claimed to have done so. Which one actually hit the jackpot? After all, a "first" cannot be achieved twice!

The two men shared a passionate commitment to polar exploration, but diverged in their attitudes and methods. Cook took a keen interest in the indigenous hunters. He strove to learn their culture and language. In contrast, Peary, who had undertaken several Arctic journeys, treated the native peoples he encountered in a manner one would never **condone** today. He approached the Arctic dwellers as a **marauder** would, **pilfering** their grave sites and selling the remains.

Cook left his base camp in Annoatok, Greenland, in February of 1908, and he claimed later that he reached the Pole on April 21 after enduring two months of brutal conditions. Once he determined his location by sextant, he began his long trek back to Annoatok, arriving there a year later. In his exhausted and emaciated state, he bore little **semblance** to a human being. Then, during his recovery, he learned that Peary had begun his own polar expedition eight months earlier, in August 1908. His

Frederick Cook

strength restored, Cook journeyed overland by sled to a Danish trading post that was 700 miles away, but he left behind most of his expedition records, intending to have them shipped later. In August 1909, several months after Cook's departure, Peary arrived at Annoatok, convinced that he had been the first to reach the Pole on April 6, 1909. Hearing that Cook was claiming to have won the race the previous year made him **irate**. This news led him to try to discredit his fellow adventurer; he later accused Cook of **fabricating** accounts of such past achievements as his successful assault on the summit of Mount McKinley. Peary even refused to take Cook's expedition records with him aboard the ship that took him home, so they were lost forever.

Cook was heartsick that his former colleague would try to **usurp** his claim with these attacks. Their friendship was now **terminated**—and thus began a lifelong **altercation**. Once back in the United States, Peary and his associates kept busy casting doubts on Cook's reliability. Cook did not take these attacks lying down. He was in Europe, writing *My Attainment of the Pole* to make his case more forcefully.

Peary stayed on the offensive and soon gained public favor. A congressional committee investigated Peary's claims, and although it passed a bill honoring him, many **dissented**, remaining unconvinced by his so-called proofs. The committee officially credited him—not with discovering the North Pole, but simply with Arctic exploration resulting in its discovery.

Both explorers claimed to have buried objects at the North Pole, but such evidence has never been found. Nor have Cook's records shown up. Both explorers have their **adherents**, and the question of who reached the Pole first remains unanswered, although Peary's name is the one that is most associated with the discovery. Peary's efforts notwithstanding, Cook's claim has proven hard to **exorcise**. One reason: More recent visitors to the polar region have confirmed as accurate his original vivid descriptions.

Audio

For iWords and audio passages, go to SadlierConnect.com.

Robert E. Peary

Definitions

Note the spelling, pronunciation, part(s) of speech, and definition(s) of each of the following words. Then write the appropriate form of the word in the blank space in the illustrative sentence(s) following.

1. abridge
(ə brij′)

(*v.*) to make shorter

Travel by air _____ the time needed to reach far-distant places.

2. altercation
(ôl tər kā′ shən)

(*n.*) an angry argument

A noisy _____ in the next apartment kept me awake for hours.

3. dissent
(di sent′)

(*v.*) to disagree; (*n.*) disagreement

Justices have an option to _____ from a ruling issued by a majority of the Supreme Court.

Some people give voice to their _____ on issues of public policy by writing letters to newspapers.

4. eminent
(em′ ə nənt)

(*adj.*) famous, outstanding, distinguished; projecting

A group of _____ scientists met to discuss long-term changes in Earth's climate.

5. fabricate
(fab′ rə kāt)

(*v.*) to make, manufacture; to make up, invent

Threads from the cocoons of caterpillars called silkworms are used to _____ silk.

6. irate
(ī rāt′)

(*adj.*) angry

Long delays caused by bad weather are likely to make even the most unflappable traveler _____.

7. pauper
(pô′ pər)

(*n.*) an extremely poor person

During the Great Depression, many people were reduced to leading the desperate lives of _____.

8. semblance
(sem′ bləns)

(*n.*) a likeness; an outward appearance; an apparition

Despite a bad case of stage fright, I tried to maintain a _____ of calm as I sang my solo.

9. **terminate**
(tər' mə nāt)

(v.) to bring to an end
If you fail to perform your job satisfactorily, your boss may _____ your employment.

10. **usurp**
(yü sərp')

(v.) to seize and hold a position by force or without right
The general who led the coup _____ the office of the duly elected president.

Using Context

*For each item, determine whether the **boldface** word from pages 38–39 makes sense in the context of the sentence. Circle the item numbers next to the six sentences in which the words are used correctly.*

1. In her speech, the business leader described how she rose from humble roots to a successful life as a **pauper**.

2. Because the first speaker at the conference gave a presentation that was much longer than its scheduled time, the second speaker had to **abridge** her remarks so that they lasted only ten minutes.

3. The insurance company will **terminate** the policy early if full payment is not made by September 1.

4. Fresh air and exercise are likely to make a person feel **irate**.

5. The expression "Fake it till you make it" suggests that you should show a **semblance** of confidence, even if you are not feeling particularly confident.

6. The goal of all the parties at the peace talks is to reach an **altercation** and move forward with the agreed-upon plan.

7. During the American Revolution, Patrick Henry, John Adams, and Samuel Adams were early voices of **dissent**, speaking out against Britain's rule of the American colonies.

8. It is perfectly fine for a fiction writer to **fabricate** stories, but it is unacceptable for a journalist to do so.

9. The plays and poems of the **eminent** writer William Shakespeare are widely regarded as some of the finest works of English literature ever written.

10. In a democracy, voters **usurp** their leaders in peaceful, orderly elections.

Choosing the Right Word

*Select the **boldface** word that better completes each sentence. You might refer to the passage on pages 36–37 to see how most of these words are used in context. Note that the choices might be related forms of the Unit words.*

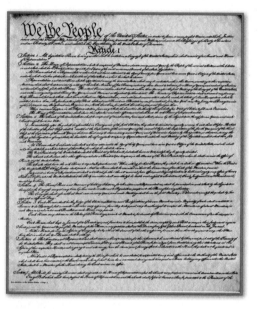

1. It is the sacred duty of all Americans to oppose any attempt to (**abridge, usurp**) or deny the rights guaranteed to us in the Constitution.

2. Either party has the right to (**terminate, fabricate**) the agreement that has been made whenever the partnership proves unprofitable.

3. I am very much flattered that you have referred to me as "an (**irate, eminent**) educator," but I prefer to think of myself as just a good teacher.

4. In a dictatorship, people who (**abridge, dissent**) from the official party line usually wind up in prison—or worse.

5. My cousin has so much imagination that he can (**dissent, fabricate**) an excuse that even an experienced principal would believe!

6. If you do not act quickly, they will (**abridge, terminate**) the agreement, and you will have to start all over again with some other company.

7. The fact that many citizens are (**eminent, irate**) over the new taxes does not mean that these taxes are unjustifiable.

8. I feel like a(n) (**usurper, pauper**) now that my part-time job has come to an end and I no longer have any spending money.

9. What began as a minor quarrel grew into a serious (**altercation, semblance**) and then into an ugly brawl.

10. You had no right to (**fabricate, usurp**) for yourself the role of gracious host at my party!

11. The few words that she grudgingly muttered were the only (**semblance, altercation**) of an apology that she offered for her rude behavior.

12. The motion to establish paid parking downtown caused great (**pauper, dissent**) among the town council members, so they postponed voting on the matter.

Completing the Sentence

Choose the word from the word bank that best completes each of the following sentences. Write the correct word or form of the word in the space provided.

abridge	dissent	fabricate	pauper	terminate
altercation	eminent	irate	semblance	usurp

1. After driving the lawful ruler out of the country for good, the villainous duke _____ the throne and crowned himself king.

2. A few of us who disagreed strongly with the committee's conclusions felt compelled to raise our voices in _____.

3. Although they have enough money to live on, the loss of most of their great wealth has left them feeling like _____.

4. To fit the newspaper article into the space available, the editor had to _____ it by omitting secondary details.

5. Although I am not a particularly argumentative person, last week I found myself involved in a heated _____ with a salesclerk.

6. After so many years of distinguished service in the United States Senate, he can properly be called a(n) _____ statesman.

7. Though I was hurt by the tactless comment, I tried to show pleasure in it by twisting my lips into a feeble _____ of a smile.

8. The only way I could _____ the argument peacefully was to walk away abruptly.

9. It is a real tribute to the ingenuity of the human mind that for thousands of years people have been _____ new and interesting artwork for the appreciation of others.

10. "I think," said the salesclerk, "that the phrase 'hot under the collar' aptly describes the typical _____ customer we have to deal with."

Definitions

Note the spelling, pronunciation, part(s) of speech, and definition(s) of each of the following words. Then write the appropriate form of the word in the blank space in the illustrative sentence(s) following.

1. adherent
(ad hēr′ ənt)

(*n.*) a follower, supporter; (*adj.*) attached, sticking to

The senator's loyal _____ campaigned long and hard for her reelection.
Before we could repaint the walls of our living room, we had to remove an _____ layer of wallpaper.

2. cherubic
(che rü′ bik)

(*adj.*) resembling an angel portrayed as a little child with a beautiful, round, or chubby face; sweet and innocent

How well those photographs of the month-old twins capture the _____ expressions on their faces!

3. condone
(kən dōn′)

(*v.*) to pardon or overlook

Our parents have always made it crystal clear to us that they do not _____ rude behavior.

4. exorcise
(ek′ sôr sīz)

(*v.*) to drive out by magic; to dispose of something troublesome, menacing, or oppressive

We must do all we can to _____ the evils of hatred and prejudice from our society.

5. gluttony
(glə′ tə nē)

(*n.*) engaging in extreme eating or drinking; greedy overindulgence

In the Middle Ages, _____ was considered one of the Seven Deadly Sins.

6. marauder
(mə rôd′ ər)

(*n.*) a raider, plunderer

Edgar Allan Poe's story "The Gold Bug" concerns treasure buried by the _____ Captain Kidd.

7. pilfer
(pil′ fər)

(*v.*) to steal in small quantities

An employee who _____ from the petty cash box will get caught sooner or later.

8. rift
(rift)

(*n.*) a split, break, breach

Failure to repay a loan can be the cause of an angry _____ between longtime friends.

9. surmount
(sər maủnt′)

(v.) to overcome, rise above

Wilma Rudolph _____ childhood illness and physical disabilities to win three Olympic gold medals.

10. trite
(trīt)

(adj.) commonplace; overused, stale

When you write an essay or a story, be especially careful to avoid using _____ expressions.

Using Context

*For each item, determine whether the **boldface** word from pages 42–43 makes sense in the context of the sentence. Circle the item numbers next to the six sentences in which the words are used correctly.*

1. The last scene of the play was so **trite** that nearly every member of the audience gasped at the turn of events.

2. By looking at the toddler's **cherubic** face, you would not have suspected that he had thrown a tantrum only minutes before.

3. The class was eager to make the exchange student feel welcome and did its best to **exorcise** a sense of warmth and encouragement on the girl's first day.

4. He realized that he must **surmount** his fear of flying if he wished to see all the sights described in the travel blog.

5. I can understand why you felt the need to lie to spare your friend's feelings, but I cannot **condone** your dishonesty.

6. The two cousins have not spoken to each other in years, although none of us knows what caused the **rift**.

7. Although Alexander Graham Bell's creation, the original telephone, has morphed over the years, it was such an important contribution that he is known as technology's greatest **marauder**.

8. To **pilfer** a few snacks from the cafeteria is to steal them, an action considered immoral by my parents.

9. The actress was beloved by many, but she now had an **adherent** reputation because of her role in a controversial film.

10. Many people like to indulge in heavy meals when on vacation, but doctors warn that even a short period of **gluttony** can have lasting effects.

Choosing the Right Word

*Select the **boldface** word that better completes each sentence. You might refer to the passage on pages 36–37 to see how most of these words are used in context. Note that the choices might be related forms of the Unit words.*

1. The fact that Abraham Lincoln was able to (**surmount, condone**) the handicap of a limited education does not mean that you should quit school.

2. One can't become a good writer just by (**surmounting, adhering**) closely to rules laid down in standard grammar books.

3. The comforting presence of relatives did much to (**exorcise, pilfer**) the patient's feelings of alarm at the thought of undergoing major surgery.

4. The robber barons of an earlier era often acted more like (**adherents, marauders**) than ethical businessmen in their dealings with the public.

5. Their (**trite, cherubic**) faces and other-worldly voices almost made me believe that the music they were singing was coming from an ethereal place.

6. Unless we repair the (**rifts, adherents**) in our party and present a united front, we will go down in crushing defeat in the upcoming election.

7. Apparently, our cat is a very successful (**marauder, rift**) who finds toys and articles of clothing in neighbors' yards and brings them all home to us.

8. I do not entirely (**exorcise, condone**) your misconduct, but I can understand, to a degree, why you behaved as you did.

9. If you ever saw how vigorously my dog attacks his food, practically inhaling it, you would understand why I accuse him of (**gluttony, adherent**).

10. Her speech was so (**cherubic, trite**) that one could almost anticipate the phrases she would use next.

11. Like all literary sneak thieves, he has a truly nasty habit of (**pilfering, surmounting**) other people's ideas and then claiming them as his own.

12. As a loyal (**adherent, gluttony**), she was horrified by her political party's stance on the issue, feeling that it went against her principles.

Completing the Sentence

Choose the word from the word bank that best completes each of the following sentences. Write the correct word or form of the word in the space provided.

adherent	**condone**	**gluttony**	**pilfer**	**surmount**
cherubic	**exorcise**	**marauder**	**rift**	**trite**

1. In this clever spoof of horror movies, the local witch doctor encounters hilarious difficulties when he tries to _____ a demon that has taken up residence in the heroine's body.

2. As the layer of clouds that hung over the city began to break up, the sun came pouring through the _____.

3. A screenplay or television drama with the same old boy-meets-girl plot can certainly be criticized as _____.

4. Bands of _____ broke through the frontier defenses of the province and began to plunder the rich farmlands of the interior.

5. In movies, characters who engage in _____ are often used for comic relief, but in real life, extreme overeating is a serious problem.

6. No one but a heartless scoundrel would _____ nickels and dimes from a charity's collection fund.

7. "That child may have an angel's _____ features, but at heart he is a little demon," I exclaimed in disgust.

8. During a recent interdenominational service in our community center, the _____ of various faiths met to worship as one.

9. "I am willing to wink at a harmless prank," the dean remarked, "but I will not _____ outright vandalism."

10. It is only through the exercise of their intelligence that people can begin to _____ the difficulties they encounter in daily living.

Synonyms

*Choose the word or form of the word from this Unit that is the same or most nearly the same in meaning as the **boldface** word or expression in the phrase. Write that word on the line. Use a dictionary if necessary.*

1. a child with an **angelic** expression _____

2. loot stolen by a mob of **bandits** _____

3. bravely faced the **enraged** crowd _____

4. did not allow political **disharmony** _____

5. programs that aid **the needy** _____

6. **condense** the story to only important details _____

7. statues of **esteemed** leaders _____

8. **commandeered** the reins of power _____

9. exhibited **voraciousness** at mealtime _____

10. a **veneer** of friendliness _____

11. **partisans** of the free market system _____

12. **turned a blind eye to** corrupt practices _____

13. **timeworn** expression on a greeting card _____

14. small change **filched** from the cash register _____

15. a disruptive **dispute** _____

Antonyms

*Choose the word or form of the word from this Unit that is most nearly opposite in meaning to the **boldface** word or expression in the phrase. Write that word on the line. Use a dictionary if necessary.*

1. a **settlement** between the two countries _____

2. **initiated** talks between the warring parties _____

3. **yielded to** many obstacles _____

4. **tear down** a third story on the house _____

5. **retain** feelings of guilt _____

Writing: Words in Action

Suppose that you are one of the explorers from the passage (pages 36–37). You want to persuade members of the National Explorers Club that you were the first to reach the North Pole. Write an argument using at least two details from the passage and three or more words from this Unit to support your claim.

Vocabulary in Context

*Some of the words you have studied in this Unit appear in **boldface** type. Read the passage below, and then circle the letter of the correct answer for each word as it is used in context.*

In 1911, Roald Amundsen of Norway and Robert Falcon Scott of England were both determined to be the first man to reach the South Pole. Both arrived at the Pole, but only one returned.

On December 14, 1911 five men arrived at the South Pole aboard three sleds. The sleds were drawn by a total of seventeen dogs and carried ample food and supplies. Roald Amundsen and his team were in good health and fine spirits as they planted a Norwegian flag in the snow—they were the first humans ever to set foot in that desolate place. They left provisions and a message in a tent and began the 800-mile journey back to base camp. They arrived on January 25, 1912 completing the round trip ten days earlier than planned.

On January 17, 1912 Captain Robert Falcon Scott's five-man British party discovered the tent. They were on foot, and each man hauled a heavy sled. They were suffering from exhaustion, severe malnutrition, and, in two cases, scurvy. After eight days' rest, they headed north. Scott kept his journal up to the end. In his last entry, dated March 29, 1912, he blamed bad weather and worse luck for the failure of his team to reach base camp. Recent researchers **dissent** from Scott's self-exculpatory verdict and conclude that the men starved to death.

It's easy to make **trite** assumptions about Scott's recklessness when he lacked the benefits of modern nutritional science. He also lacked a good cook and relied on canned food while Amundsen's cook, Adolf Lindström, made tasty, well-balanced meals that promoted Norwegian good health and **cherubic** faces. Manhauling a sledge required at least 7,000 calories a day, which for an average person is **gluttony**. But on their **pauper's** ration of 4,400 calories Scott's men lost, on average, 55 pounds of bodyweight. Even in his final journal entries, Scott insisted that his food supplies were sufficient—a claim that is impossible to **condone**.

---

1. To **dissent** from a verdict is to
- **a.** defer
- **b.** demur
- **c.** disagree
- **d.** deny

2. To be **trite** is to be
- **a.** false
- **b.** unfounded
- **c.** stale
- **d.** flippant

3. Faces that are **cherubic**, as the Norwegians' are said to be, are usually
- **a.** immature
- **b.** chubby
- **c.** good-natured
- **d.** inventive

4. The word **gluttony** most nearly means
- **a.** overeating
- **b.** hunger
- **c.** austerity
- **d.** jealousy

5. A person is said to be a **pauper** if he or she is
- **a.** wealthy
- **b.** thin
- **c.** foreign
- **d.** impoverished

6. To **condone** Scott's conduct is to
- **a.** pardon it
- **b.** agree with it
- **c.** like it
- **d.** ignore it

Vocabulary for Comprehension
Part 1

*Read this passage, which contains words in **boldface** that appear in Units 1–3. Then choose the best answer to each question based on what is stated or implied in the passage. You may refer to the passage as often as necessary.*

Questions 1–10 are based on the following passage.

More than a decade ago, "farm-to-table" restaurants began to **proliferate** in the United States. At such restaurants, menus offer an appealing array of locally sourced
(5) meat and produce and often boast that these foods are "naturally raised," "sustainable," and organic. In today's world, it seems, diners are increasingly concerned about the origins of their food.
(10) People want to eat meat and vegetables raised on local farms—preferably small, family-run businesses—where only the best, most environmentally sound, and humane methods are employed.

(15) The lure of farm-to-table cooking is undeniable, but its very premise may cloak a fundamental contradiction. Americans do indeed wish to eat local food. This desire may **predispose** them to
(20) believe the stories on restaurant menus. But consumers also have a longstanding **gluttony** for cheap food, which would seem to undermine the economic foundation of farm-to-table dining, for
(25) locally grown meat and produce are anything but cheap. A single egg, if laid by a happy, free-roaming hen, might be worth a dollar. To put that in perspective, supermarkets might sell a dozen eggs for
(30) 99¢. A steak that comes from a pasture-fed steer might carry a $40 price tag to a customer's plate—far more than what most diners are willing to pay. Most restaurants cannot fairly **compensate**
(35) local farmers for their costs without drastically raising menu prices, which would drive away restaurant customers.

More contradictions underlie the farm-to-table trend. Most food that
(40) Americans eat is seasonal, but diners have grown accustomed to eating what they want, *when* they want—strawberries in winter, lamb in fall, tomatoes all year round. If diners insist on buying meals
(45) containing ingredients that are out of season, chefs must necessarily bypass their local purveyors. Customers are unlikely to notice the difference, since the **semblance** of chicken on the plate—local
(50) or foreign, free range or factory farm—is hardly distinctive. Limited resources present another problem. Most restaurants buy dozens, if not hundreds, of kinds of food each month. To source even half
(55) of them locally would require a huge commitment of time and money. Chefs would have to find the farms, test their products, negotiate prices, and arrange deliveries while continuing to run their
(60) kitchens, manage staffs, and plan menus.

So it may come as no surprise that many of the claims found on the menus of farm-to-table restaurants are **spurious**. In a painstaking piece of investigative
(65) journalism, a *Tampa Bay Times* reporter checked restaurant menus and invoices, researching where the food actually originated. What she found created a firestorm in the restaurant world. Much
(70) of the "locally sourced" food was, in fact, purchased through the normal global supply chain. Some restaurants made honest mistakes on their menus. Many others **fabricated** stories of local origin.
(75) A chef might purchase beef from a local farmer once, then return to his normal corporate supplier while prominently

featuring the farmer's name on his menu for years to come. Indignant farmers point (80) out that such misrepresentations are **lucrative** for restaurants in the short run. But they create a **breach** of confidence among customers that could permanently damage the marketplace.

1. The main purpose of the passage is to
   A) describe the farm-to-table movement.
   B) explain the benefits of eating locally produced food.
   C) highlight the work of an investigative journalist.
   D) expose problems in the farm-to-table movement.

2. As it is used in line 2, "proliferate" most nearly means to
   A) reproduce.
   B) spread rapidly.
   C) succeed.
   D) engage in deceit.

3. The "stories on restaurant menus" (line 20) refer to
   A) claims that food is locally sourced.
   B) food sold at artificially low prices.
   C) organic certification.
   D) customer reviews.

4. The author includes the supermarket price of a dozen eggs to
   A) show it is similar to the cost of free-range eggs.
   B) explain why farm-to-table cuisine is expensive.
   C) raise doubts about the pricing of farm-to-table restaurant food.
   D) support local chicken farmers.

5. Which choice provides the best evidence for the answer to the previous question?
   A) Lines 33–37 ("Most . . . customers")
   B) Lines 38–39 ("More . . . trend")
   C) Lines 39–42 ("Most . . . want—")
   D) Lines 44–47 ("If diners . . . purveyors")

6. As it is used in line 49, "semblance" most nearly means
   A) likeness.
   B) apparition.
   C) outward appearance.
   D) culinary appeal.

7. How do the "limited resources" in line 51 present a problem for farm-to-table chefs?
   A) Chefs cannot afford the cost of local food.
   B) Customers will not pay the true cost of locally sourced food.
   C) Restaurants owners cannot pay the salaries of good chefs.
   D) Chefs do not have the time or money to find local suppliers.

8. What point does the author make by including paragraph 4 (lines 61–84)?
   A) Investigative journalists are good at uncovering the truth.
   B) Many farm-to-table claims are false.
   C) Farm-to-table restaurants are profitable.
   D) Farmers are glad to sell to local restaurants.

9. As it is used in line 74, "fabricated" most nearly means
   A) made up.
   B) manufactured.
   C) exaggerated.
   D) advertised.

10. According to the passage, why are farmers "indignant" (line 79)?
    A) They do not earn much from restaurants.
    B) Diners do not want to pay the true cost of local foods.
    C) Their names are being used but not their products.
    D) Chefs are dishonest.

Vocabulary for Comprehension
Part 2

*Read this passage, which contains words in **boldface** that appear in Units 1–3. Then choose the best answer to each question based on what is stated or implied in the passage. You may refer to the passage as often as necessary.*

Questions 1–10 are based on the following passage.

John Dickinson was born in Maryland, grew up in Delaware, and studied law in London. He began working as a lawyer in Philadelphia in 1757. By the time he wrote

(5) his *Letters from a Farmer in Pennsylvania to the Inhabitants of the British Colonies,* Dickinson was an **eminent** colonial statesman. He wrote the letters in response to the Townshend Acts. They

(10) were passed by the British government in 1767. In its **perennial** quest for revenue, Parliament had imposed levies, or taxes, on colonial imports of lead, glass, paper, paint, and tea. (Tea, remember, was the

(15) principal beverage of the colonies.) The Acts also established a hated machinery for collecting the taxes in American ports. Coast guard ships, spies, officers, and searchers—all financed by money

(20) extracted from colonial pocketbooks— were employed in the new bureaucracy.

For Dickinson, the decrees posed a **dilemma**. The Acts were so unjust as to force citizens of good conscience to

(25) consider disobedience. Yet Dickinson, like most colonial leaders at the time, still considered himself a loyal Englishman and sincerely hoped that differences with the British could be **surmounted**.

(30) In his second letter, Dickinson **admonished** Parliament for exceeding its authority. Britain had a right to levy taxes, but only in the interest of regulating trade. "If you ONCE admit," warns Dickinson,

(35) "that Great Britain may lay duties upon her exportations to us, *for the purpose of levying money on us only,* she then will . . . lay those duties on the articles which she

prohibits us to manufacture—and the

(40) tragedy of American liberty is finished." Not only was Britain using the colonies as a source of cash, but it was also stifling American industry and freedom. Even more damning, Parliament lacked a legal

(45) basis for imposing such levies. In his memorable fourth letter, Dickinson wrote:

That it is *inseparably essential to the freedom of a people, and the undoubted right of Englishmen,* that NO TAX be

(50) imposed on them, *except with their own consent*, given personally, or by their representatives...

That the only representatives of the people of the colonies, are the persons chosen

(55) therein by themselves; and that NO TAXES ever have been, or can be constitutionally imposed on them, but by their respective legislatures.

Often reduced to the **trite** expression

(60) "no taxation without representation," Dickinson's argument would become a cornerstone of revolutionary thinking.

Colonial freedom—and Britain's gradual encroachment upon it—were persistent

(65) themes for Dickinson. "All artful rulers," he wrote, "who strive to extend their power beyond its just limits, endeavor to give to their attempts as much semblance of legality as possible." Colonists needed to

(70) recognize these maneuvers as attempts to constrain the liberties of British citizens who happened to live in America. Dickinson's **unflinching** criticism of the Townshend Acts provided **fodder** for a

(75) public still angry about the Stamp Act (another attempt to boost the British treasury on the backs of colonial

taxpayers). Printed as pamphlets, distributed throughout the colonies, and (80) published in many newspapers, Dickinson's letters served to **fortify** Americans' suspicions about British motives and paved the way for revolution.

1. The main purpose of this passage is to
A) describe key events in Dickinson's life.
B) show the importance of Dickinson's letters.
C) overview the Townshend Acts.
D) explain why Parliament's taxes were unconstitutional.

2. As it is used in line 11, "perennial" most nearly means
A) persistent.
B) annual.
C) tyrannical.
D) unfair.

3. What point does the author make by including paragraph 2 (lines 22–29)?
A) The Townshend Acts were unjust.
B) Dickinson was forced to consider disobedience.
C) Most colonial leaders were ready for revolution.
D) Dickinson was still a loyal Englishman who hoped for conciliation with Britain.

4. As it is used in line 31, "admonished" most nearly means
A) cautioned against.
B) scolded.
C) reminded of a duty.
D) wrote to.

5. In lines 30–40, Dickinson expresses his concerns that
A) British rule will come to an end.
B) England is raising tax money from the colonies and using it to police them.
C) the Townshend Acts will force a revolt.
D) England taxes goods it will not allow the colonies to make for themselves.

6. The author quotes from Dickinson's fourth letter to
A) give a sample of Dickinson's writing.
B) demonstrate Dickinson's logic.
C) show the letter's recognition of what would be a key cause of the revolution.
D) explain why Dickinson disliked taxes and so rallied the colonies to revolt.

7. According to Dickinson, what is a critical aspect of freedom?
A) People give their consent to taxation.
B) Colonists send representatives to Parliament.
C) Every colonist votes.
D) Englishmen reject unconstitutional Parliamentary laws.

8. Which choice provides the best evidence for the answer to the previous question?
A) Lines 43–45 ("Even . . . levies")
B) Lines 47–52 ("That . . . representatives")
C) Lines 53–55 ("That . . . themselves")
D) Lines 55–58 ("NO . . . legislatures")

9. As it is used in line 74, "fodder" most nearly means
A) food for livestock.
B) raw material for a purpose.
C) argument.
D) excuse.

10. In lines 73–83, the author argues that Dickinson
A) cared about freedom.
B) criticized the Townshend Acts.
C) influenced colonial thinking in the pre-Revolutionary years.
D) published his letters in pamphlets and newspapers.

Synonyms

*From the word bank below, choose the word that has the same or nearly the same meaning as the **boldface** word in each sentence and write it on the line. You will not use all of the words.*

adjourn	diffuse	irate	predispose
breach	eminent	marauder	proliferate
cherubic	gluttony	opinionated	spasmodic
comely	illegible	perennial	terse

1. The candidate's **brief** replies during the interview left the reporter wondering if he was hiding something. _____

2. Gwendolyn is an **attractive** young woman whose charming appearance is accompanied by a strong personality and self-satisfied manner. _____

3. The store clerk was not comfortable dealing with the **infuriated** customer, so he asked the manager to take charge of the situation. _____

4. In movies about the American West, sheriffs are constantly on the lookout for bank robbers, horse thieves, and a **looter** or two. _____

5. I hope you won't accuse me of **overeating** if I ask for an extra-large helping of dessert. _____

6. The meeting will **discontinue** promptly at 3:00 p.m., and any remaining agenda items will be addressed tomorrow morning. _____

7. The doctor is not only one of the world's most **famous** oceanographers but also a well-known advocate for protecting coral reefs and other marine habitats. _____

8. In the absence of predators, the population of prey animals will **multiply**, creating an ecologically unhealthy imbalance. _____

9. Hockey is a **recurring** source of disagreement for my neighbor and me and therefore a subject we never discuss. _____

10. The infant looked particularly **angelic** as he slept in his pale-blue pajamas decorated with pictures of sheep. _____

11. The signature at the bottom of the painting was **unreadable**, so we have no idea who the artist was. _____

12. The frosted glass lampshade will cover that bare bulb and also **scatter** its light. _____

Two-Word Completions

Select the pair of words that best completes the meaning of each of the following sentences.

1. Though I am prepared to wink at an occasional petty offense against my moral code, I absolutely refuse to _____ behavior that is consistently wicked or _____.

   a. exorcise . . . circumspect
   b. abridge . . . unbridled
   c. condone . . . dissolute
   d. efface . . . erratic

2. He was thrown out of the club for constantly _____ small items from the supply room. According to club rules, that type of petty theft constitutes valid grounds for _____.

   a. fabricating . . . admonishment
   b. pilfering . . . expulsion
   c. tantalizing . . . termination
   d. sullying . . . subjugation

3. Though he began life little better than a(n) _____, with only his hands in his pockets, his highly _____ business deals turned him into a multimillionaire before the age of forty.

   a. usurper . . . spurious
   b. adherent . . . cumbersome
   c. pauper . . . lucrative
   d. brigand . . . mediocre

4. The earthquake had more or less reduced our house to a pile of worthless rubble. Nevertheless, we picked carefully through the _____, trying to _____ items of value. Unfortunately, very little could be saved.

   a. muddle . . . efface
   b. deadlock . . . relinquish
   c. dilemma . . . condone
   d. debris . . . salvage

5. "If you always act cautiously, you should be able to _____ many of life's obstacles," Dad told me. "Still, some difficulties cannot be overcome, even by the most _____ behavior."

   a. abridge . . . alien
   b. surmount . . . circumspect
   c. relinquish . . . mediocre
   d. commandeer . . . erratic

6. Although the auditorium was packed with the candidate's supporters, who greeted his remarks with thunderous cheers and applause, there were a few _____ in the crowd who seemed inclined only to boo and _____.

   a. adherents . . . admonish
   b. paupers . . . condone
   c. dissenters . . . jeer
   d. brigands . . . feint

7. Minor squabbles may cause temporary _____ in our friendship, but such _____, however heated and noisy, have never resulted in a permanent breach.

   a. rifts . . . altercations
   b. deadlocks . . . abridgments
   c. dissents . . . semblances
   d. feints . . . dilemmas

Idioms

In the essay about the controversy over whether Robert Peary or Frederick Cook was first to reach the North Pole (see pages 36–37), the author asks the question "Which one actually hit the jackpot?"

"Hit the jackpot" is an idiom that means "succeed" or "win the prize." An **idiom** is an informal expression or figure of speech that means something different from the literal meaning of the words that form it. Because the meanings of idioms are not obvious or self-explanatory, they must be learned, just like new or unfamiliar words.

Choosing the Right Idiom

*Read each sentence. Use context clues to figure out the meaning of each idiom in **boldface**. Then write the letter of the definition for the idiom in the sentence.*

1. One judge at the dog show was very skinny. He must **eat like a bird.**_____

2. After much training, the dog finally **got the hang of it.**_____

3. Ranchers who do not use guardian dogs for their herds are **skating on thin ice.**_____

4. After a long day directing sheep, my collie just wanted to get back home and **hit the hay.**_____

5. The value of good herding dogs to a shepherd is **as plain as the nose on your face.**_____

6. After losing sheep, it **dawned on** the farmer that she needed more dogs to protect the flock._____

7. To **make ends meet**, Lefty Smalls rents his land to a neighbor to graze her sheep._____

8. I buy herding dogs from a trainer who **drives a hard bargain.**_____

9. When her dog did not win first prize, the young girl was **down in the dumps.**_____

10. The awkward new ranch hand **is all thumbs.**_____

a. taking a dangerous chance

b. learned how to do something

c. go to bed

d. began to grow plain

e. discouraged

f. makes a deal to one's advantage

g. very clumsy

h. something that is obvious

i. earn enough to pay one's bills

j. consume very little food

Classical Roots

pos, pon—to put, place

The root *pos* appears in **predispose** (page 14). The literal meaning is "to put away before," but the word has come to mean "to incline" or "to make susceptible." Some other words based on the same root are listed below.

component	depose	impose	repository
composite	disposition	juxtapose	transpose

From the list of words above, choose the one that corresponds to each of the brief definitions below. Write the word in the blank space in the illustrative sentence below the definition. Use an online or print dictionary if necessary.

1. a part, element

At the last minute we replaced a central _____ of our presentation.

2. to place side by side or close together (*"to place next to"*)

They will _____ incongruous celebrity photos in order to make a lampoon.

3. a place where things are stored or kept

They rented an off-site warehouse as a _____ for company records.

4. to put out of office; to declare under oath (*"to put down"*)

She was shocked to learn of a secret plot to _____ the king.

5. to interchange positions; to shift

Jeff will _____ the harmony into a different key that better suits the singer's voice.

6. made up of distinct parts; combining elements or characteristics; such a combination (*"put together"*)

The forensic artist made a _____ drawing of the primary suspect.

7. to put or place upon or over something else

Digital software allows creative photographers to _____ a second image over the first to create an original picture.

8. one's temperament; a tendency, inclination; a settlement, arrangement

That pony's pleasing _____ makes it a perfect choice for children.

*Read the following passage, taking note of the **boldface** words and their contexts. These words are among those you will be studying in Unit 4. It may help you to complete the exercises in this Unit if you refer to the way the words are used below.*

Elephant Culture and Conservation
<Expository Writing>

Throughout history, humans have admired elephants for their strength, their intelligence, and their courageous, **intrepid** behavior. The largest land mammal, elephants are divided into two species, named for the continents on which each is found. The African elephant (*Loxodonta africana*) stands twelve feet high and weighs up to eight tons. The Asian elephant (*Elephas maximus*) is slightly less massive. For centuries, Asian elephants have been carefully trained to perform the most **arduous** of tasks, such as carrying heavy loads and patrolling protected forests over rough terrain. Asian elephants have proved more **pliant** than the African species. They can respond to more than thirty vocal commands from their handlers, called *mahawats* in India.

Elephants are highly social creatures, living in herds under the leadership of a matriarch. Without the coordination this senior female provides, **anarchy** might prevail in the herd. The animals show affection by wrapping their trunks around one another, and they are especially attentive to the young calves. Elephants sleep little because they are always on the move in search of far-flung sources of food and water. In Africa, drought is a herd's biggest threat. Recently, elephants have been shown to communicate using infrasound—deep rumbles inaudible to the human ear—to ensure **access** to water and to keep the herd together. Elephants are peaceful animals, with no natural predators except humans. An elephant's trunk is a remarkable limb that could serve as an ancient **prototype** for a modern precision tool. Two fingers at the end of the trunk are so delicate that an elephant can hold an egg without breaking it.

There is one appendage, however, that critically endangers elephants: their ivory tusks. The tusks have made elephants vulnerable to poaching in both Africa and Asia. Poachers employ a variety of brutal methods to kill a wild elephant. They then slash off the animals' tusks for the illegal ivory trade and **abscond** with their loot, a clear-cut case of **larceny**.

It has proved especially difficult to **disentangle** the complex issues surrounding poaching and the ivory trade, a practice that puts all elephants at risk. The threat to elephants is serious enough to have made them one of the chief concerns of wildlife conservationists, especially in Asia.

Asian elephants are strong work animals that can be trained to carry heavy loads.

To discourage poaching and the illegal trade in ivory, Kenyan authorities destroyed $3 million worth of elephant tusks.

Elephas maximus. In Africa, certain countries assert that they have too many elephants. These countries have, therefore, devised culling campaigns to reduce the herds. Such programs are **reviled** as cruel by many conservationists, who warn that elephants are teetering on a **precipice** that could lead to extinction. So though it is said that an elephant never forgets, it appears that people might forget the elephant. The many challenges posed by conservation efforts are **daunting**. Are these majestic animals **fated** to suffer extinction? Or can well-designed conservation programs afford them a **reprieve** from such a bleak future? In 1989, conservationist Richard Leakey convinced Kenya's president to kick off a vigorous antipoaching campaign by publicly **incinerating** a 12-ton pile of elephant tusks. The pile was 20 feet high and worth $3 million. This celebrated bonfire drew worldwide attention.

Advocates of tough antipoaching laws argue that only severe penalties will **rectify** the situation and ease the threat to Asian elephants, now numbering only 30,000 to 50,000 spread over thirteen countries. India has the largest population by far. Fortunately, elephants have an **auspicious** reputation in India, and in 1992, it established Project Elephant as a national agency to protect

Audio

For iWords and audio passages, go to SadlierConnect.com.

Definitions

Note the spelling, pronunciation, part(s) of speech, and definition(s) of each of the following words. Then write the appropriate form of the word in the blank space in the illustrative sentence(s) following.

1. anarchy
(an' ər kē)

(*n.*) a lack of government and law; confusion
In the final days of a war, civilians may find themselves living in _____.

2. auspicious
(ô spish' əs)

(*adj.*) favorable; fortunate
My parents describe the day that they first met as a most_____ occasion.

3. daunt
(dônt)

(*v.*) to overcome with fear, intimidate; to dishearten, discourage
Despite all its inherent dangers, space flight did not _____ the Mercury program astronauts.

4. hoodwink
(hùd' wiŋk)

(*v.*) to mislead by a trick, swindle
Many sweepstakes offers _____ people into thinking they have already won big prizes.

5. inanimate
(in an' ə mit)

(*adj.*) not having life; without energy or spirit
Although fossils are _____, they hold many clues to life on Earth millions of years ago.

6. incinerate
(in sin' ər āt)

(*v.*) to burn to ashes
Because of environmental concerns, many cities and towns no longer _____ their garbage.

7. larceny
(lär' sə nē)

(*n.*) theft
Someone who steals property that is worth thousands of dollars commits grand _____.

8. pliant
(plī' ənt)

(*adj.*) bending readily; easily influenced
The _____ branches of the sapling sagged but did not break under the weight of the heavy snow.

9. prototype
(prō′ tə tīp)

(n.) an original model on which later versions are patterned
The assembly line managers studied the
_____ of the new car for weeks before
production began.

10. rectify
(rek′ tə fī)

(v.) to make right, correct
The senators debated a series of measures designed
to _____ the nation's trade imbalance.

Using Context

*For each item, determine whether the **boldface** word from pages 58–59 makes sense in the context of the sentence. Circle the item numbers next to the six sentences in which the words are used correctly.*

1. A sincere apology will often **rectify** a conflict or problem that was caused by a genuine mistake.

2. The citizens of that country are looking forward to peace and reconstruction, following several years of civil war and **anarchy**.

3. I am determined to set up this equipment by myself, and I will not let either my lack of experience or the confusing directions in the manual **daunt** me.

4. Racers have been known to **hoodwink** their vehicles in preparation for the slick pavement and curves in the road.

5. Many people think that cats and dogs are **inanimate**, but, in fact, they often get along well with each other and can even become good friends.

6. The game was far from over, but with a 15-point lead at the end of the first quarter, our team was off to an **auspicious** start.

7. Local officials evacuated the hillside cabins, fearing that the spreading wildfire might **incinerate** them.

8. The anonymous million-dollar donation to the university was an unexpected and much appreciated act of **larceny**.

9. The designers will examine the **prototype** of the new toy and decide whether it needs changes or is approved.

10. Diamonds are so **pliant** that they are used to make blades that can slice through steel, concrete, and other hard-to-cut materials.

Choosing the Right Word

*Select the **boldface** word that better completes each sentence. You might refer to the passage on pages 56–57 to see how most of these words are used in context. Note that the choices might be related forms of the Unit words.*

1. The voters may seem unaware of the underlying issues, but in the long run they cannot be (**rectified, hoodwinked**) by self-serving politicians.

2. There is a vast difference between democracy, under which everyone has duties and privileges, and (**larceny, anarchy**), under which no one has.

3. When her eyes suddenly blazed with such fury, I felt that the heat of her glance would all but (**hoodwink, incinerate**) me.

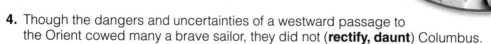

4. Though the dangers and uncertainties of a westward passage to the Orient cowed many a brave sailor, they did not (**rectify, daunt**) Columbus.

5. We should begin studying foreign languages at an early age because it is during those years that our minds are most (**auspicious, pliant**) and receptive.

6. Spring, with its ever-renewing promise of life, is for me the most (**inanimate, auspicious**) of seasons.

7. Although she looks young and inexperienced, it is not easy to (**hoodwink, rectify**) her, since she is a private detective by profession.

8. At the design firm, the most well-received (**larcenies, prototypes**) for the new line of evening gowns were the ones made from a new silk blend.

9. The team of accountants spent hours trying to locate and then to (**rectify, daunt**) the error I had so carelessly made.

10. A great playwright's characters always seem to come alive; those of a third-rate hack stubbornly remain (**pliant, inanimate**).

11. Anyone who takes the writings of other people and presents them as his or her own is guilty of literary (**larceny, anarchy**).

12. His broad education gave him an (**auspicious, inanimate**) view of cultures different from his own.

Completing the Sentence

Choose the word from the word bank that best completes each of the following sentences. Write the correct word or form of the word in the space provided.

anarchy	daunt	inanimate	larceny	prototype
auspicious	hoodwink	incinerate	pliant	rectify

1. With no government around to restore order, the small country remained in a state of _____ for weeks after the revolution.

2. His extraordinary faith in his own abilities enabled her to overcome many obstacles that would have _____ someone less confident.

3. Though many people firmly believe that life-forms exist somewhere in outer space, everything that our astronauts have so far encountered has been decidedly _____.

4. Though somewhat massively built, the gymnast's body was as supple and _____ as a ballet dancer's.

5. The steak I'd accidentally left in the broiler too long wasn't just overdone; it was positively _____.

6. This handmade chair is a(n) _____ for the machine-built ones we will produce by the thousands.

7. As soon as I discovered that the project was being mismanaged, I tried my best to _____ the situation.

8. No matter how much protective legislation we pass, there will probably always be gullible consumers for swindlers to _____.

9. The youths who had "borrowed" the car for joyriding were caught by the police and charged with _____.

10. Since everything had gone so smoothly, we felt that the campaign to elect Ellen captain was off to a(n) _____ beginning.

Definitions

Note the spelling, pronunciation, part(s) of speech, and definition(s) of each of the following words. Then write the appropriate form of the word in the blank space in the illustrative sentence(s) following.

1. abscond
(ab skänd')

(*v.*) to run off and hide

The thieves who _____ with several of the museum's most valuable paintings have never been found.

2. access
(ak' ses)

(*n.*) approach or admittance to places, persons, things; an increase; (*v.*) to get at, obtain

_____ to information on a seemingly unlimited number of topics is available over the Internet.

You need a password in order to _____ your email accounts.

3. arduous
(är' jü əs)

(*adj.*) hard to do, requiring much effort

No matter how carefully you plan for it, moving to a new home is an _____ chore.

4. disentangle
(dis en taŋ' gəl)

(*v.*) to free from tangles or complications

Rescuers worked for hours to _____ a whale from the fishing net wrapped around its jaws.

5. fated
(fā' tid)

(*adj.*) determined in advance by destiny or fortune

The tragic outcome of Shakespeare's *Romeo and Juliet* is _____ from the play's very first scene.

6. intrepid
(in trep' id)

(*adj.*) very brave, fearless, unshakable

_____ Polynesian sailors in outrigger canoes were the first humans to reach the Hawaiian Islands.

7. pompous
(päm' pəs)

(*adj.*) overly self-important in speech and manner; excessively stately or ceremonious

Political cartoonists like nothing better than to mock _____ public officials.

8. precipice
(pres' ə pis)

(*n.*) a very steep cliff; the brink or edge of disaster

During the Cuban Missile Crisis, the world hovered on the_____ of nuclear war

9. reprieve
(ri prēv′)

(n.) a temporary relief or delay; (v.) to grant a postponement

A vacation is a kind of _____ from the cares and responsibilities of everyday life.

A judge may _____ a first-time offender from jail time until sentencing.

10. revile
(ri vīl′)

(v.) to attack with words, call bad names

The enraged King Lear _____ the daughters who have cast him out into a fierce storm.

Using Context

*For each item, determine whether the **boldface** word from pages 62–63 makes sense in the context of the sentence. Circle the item numbers next to the six sentences in which the words are used correctly.*

1. The author is delighted by the response to her first novel, which critics **revile** nearly universally.

2. I was unable to gain **access** to the library's newspaper archives, but luckily I found the information I needed online.

3. The mountain climber fell into a deep **precipice** and was trapped for hours before being rescued.

4. Although his natural talents and charm suggested he was **fated** to be an actor, he also put in many hours of hard work.

5. Only a dishonest and unscrupulous person would be tempted to **abscond** with the money from the fundraiser.

6. Even though her accomplishments were impressive, her **pompous** attitude irritated everyone so much that she did not get the job.

7. After many days of intense heat, the short rainfall was a welcome **reprieve**.

8. You are such a skilled artist that you make even the most complex scene seem **arduous** to paint.

9. I had spent many hours rehearsing and preparing for this moment, but I felt **intrepid** and shaky as I approached the audition room.

10. Please do not **disentangle** the garden hose into a mire of kinks and coils.

Choosing the Right Word

*Select the **boldface** word that better completes each sentence. You might refer to the passage on pages 56–57 to see how most of these words are used in context. Note that the choices might be related forms of the Unit words.*

1. Like farmers separating the wheat from the chaff, the members of a jury must (**disentangle, revile**) the truth from the evidence presented to them.

2. Only by admitting your fault and trying to make up for it can you obtain a(n) (**reprieve, access**) from the pangs of conscience.

3. Instead of recognizing that she caused her own troubles, she continues to (**revile, abscond**) all the people who were "unfair" to her.

4. Despite the threats made against his life, the (**arduous, intrepid**) district attorney was able to obtain a conviction of the corrupt official.

5. My aunt can be so (**pompous, intrepid**) when she lectures me about politics.

6. How can you accuse me of (**absconding, reviling**) with all your brilliant ideas when you have never had an original thought in your life?

7. To (**access, disentangle**) the large safe we will need the five-digit combination to the lock.

8. His speech and manners were so (**arduous, pompous**) and stiff that he cut a somewhat ridiculous figure at our informal little get-together.

9. The general feared that the latest attacks on the city would push the situation over the (**precipice, access**), leading directly to a full-blown war.

10. Although the hero and the heroine were parted by circumstance, I knew that they were (**intrepid, fated**) to meet again before the last commercial.

11. Far from being useless, mathematics will give you (**reprieve, access**) to many fields of scientific study.

12. For most retired athletes, the comeback trail is a(n) (**arduous, fated**) one, and few ever get to the end of it.

Completing the Sentence

Choose the word from the word bank that best completes each of the following sentences. Write the correct word or form of the word in the space provided.

abscond	arduous	fated	pompous	reprieve
access	disentangle	intrepid	precipice	revile

1. The treasurer who had _____ with the company's funds was quickly captured by alert federal agents.

2. Without the slightest hesitation, _____ firefighters will enter a blazing building to rescue anyone who may be trapped.

3. This master key will give you _____ to any of the rooms in the building.

4. The overly ornate style of many eighteenth-century writers seems rather forced and _____ to us today.

5. Since I'm only an average linguist, mastering the irregular verbs in French was one of the most _____ tasks I have ever undertaken.

6. Since I did not feel well prepared, the three-day postponement of final exams was a most welcome _____.

7. One of the most controversial figures of his time, the former president was revered by some and _____ by others.

8. The film had gotten so badly entwined in the malfunctioning old movie projector that I had a hard time _____ it.

9. Ancient astrologers developed the idea that what is _____ to happen to a person is determined by the stars.

10. The guardrail was reinforced to prevent cars from skidding over the edge of the _____ and falling into the abyss below.

Synonyms

Choose the word or form of the word from this Unit that is the same or most nearly the same in meaning as the boldface word or expression in the phrase. Write that word on the line. Use a dictionary if necessary.

1. a house built on a **promontory** _____
2. an **inert** stone _____
3. **unravel** the twisted yarn _____
4. granted a thirty-day **deferral** _____
5. **ostentatious** style of dress _____
6. the **first example** of the new invention _____
7. **courageous** in the face of danger _____
8. **burn** the waste material _____
9. editorials that **denounced** the mayor's actions _____
10. **unnerved** by the spinning roller coaster _____
11. scheduled to stand trial for **burglary** _____
12. **made off** with the store's jewels _____
13. **duped** into buying a flawed diamond _____
14. gained **entrée** to an exclusive club _____
15. tried to **remedy** their mistaken impression of me _____

Antonyms

*Choose the word or form of the word from this Unit that is most nearly opposite in meaning to the **boldface** word or expression in the phrase. Write that word on the line. Use a dictionary if necessary.*

1. the **effortless** ascent up the mountain _____
2. a series of **ominous** events _____
3. an **accidental** meeting _____
4. bent the **rigid** rubber sole _____
5. a city in a state of **law and order** _____

Writing: Words in Action

In a brief essay, explain some of the challenges people and organizations face in their efforts to save endangered animals. Use specific examples from your observations, studies, reading (refer to pages 56–57), or personal experiences. Use three or more words from this Unit to support your response.

Vocabulary in Context

*Some of the words you have studied in this Unit appear in **boldface** type. Read the passage below, and then circle the letter of the correct answer for each word as it is used in context.*

The Congo Basin, a vast forested region in central Africa, is one of the most biodiverse regions on the planet. One species of animals, the forest elephant, plays a critical role in maintaining the health of this tropical ecosystem. With their massive bulk, the elephants engineer networks of trails through the forests. Other animals, such as giant hogs and antelopes, travel along these trails to avoid **arduous** treks through the thick understory, the layer of vegetation under the main canopy of the forest. The elephants eat huge quantities of fruit from a range of trees, dispersing the seeds in their dung and thus ensuring the regeneration of trees. Minerals are also an important part of the elephants' diet, so the animals create clearings along rivers where mineral deposits occur. These clearings are used as watering holes by dozens of species.

Because the forest is practically impenetrable, **access** is difficult, and relatively little is known about the forest elephant. Until recently, scientists considered the forest elephant and the larger savannah elephant to be members of the same species. Genetic analysis has confirmed that the two elephants are distinct.

Unfortunately, governments in the region have been plagued with instability and corruption, a situation that makes forest elephants vulnerable to poaching. Local officials, often **pompous** and greedy, can be persuaded to allow heavily-armed outsiders into national parks. The poachers may **hoodwink** surrounding communities into supplying guides to locate elephant herds. Hiding around forest clearings, the poachers wait until elephants gather to eat, drink, and socialize. The resulting slaughter can be staggering. After one such massacre, researchers discovered the **inanimate** bodies of twenty-six elephants, all missing their tusks. The poachers were able to **abscond**, loading the ivory into a waiting truck.

---

1. An **arduous** trek takes
   a. much time
   b. great effort
   c. determination
   d. planning

2. **Access** to a forest is a way to
   a. enter it
   b. skirt it
   c. study it
   d. appreciate it

3. The word **pompous** most nearly means
   a. self-important
   b. corrupt
   c. clever
   d. humble

4. If you **hoodwink** people, you
   a. convince them
   b. encourage them
   c. mislead them
   d. frighten them

5. An **inanimate** body is
   a. decomposing
   b. lifeless
   c. massive
   d. tragic

6. To **abscond** is to
   a. succeed
   b. profit
   c. steal
   d. run off

*Read the following passage, taking note of the **boldface** words and their contexts. These words are among those you will be studying in Unit 5. It may help you to complete the exercises in this Unit if you refer to the way the words are used below.*

The Leopard: Unlikely Survivor
<Expository Essay>

"A leopard cannot change its spots." So runs a well-known proverb. But this statement is easily **rebutted**. It turns out that leopards are remarkably adaptable animals whose **latent** ability to adapt to new situations has made them one of the few big cats not facing extinction in the wild. Africa, the Middle East, Asia, and Russia all have leopard populations. Half a million leopards roam in areas as different as the plains of South Africa to the snows of the Russian Far East. That's as many leopards as there are cheetahs, lions, and tigers combined. The leopard ranks first among cats in its ability to survive.

A **paramount** factor in the leopard's success is its diet—this cat is a generalist. The leopard does not discriminate when it comes to food, and the list of its many prey seems almost **arbitrary**: Baboons, lizards, insects, and antelope are all possible meals. Cats whose diets are limited to a few species are in danger when populations of their favored prey dwindle.

Their wide-ranging diet also means that leopards can live in different types of ecosystems. Species that can only survive in a specific landscape have one of two choices when their habitats shrink or become overpopulated: **exodus** or death. Polar bears, for example, can only exist in very cold climates, and they are in danger of losing that habitat. However, leopards can live in jungles, where they eat monkeys; islands, where they eat fish; and mountains, where they eat rodents. This wide-ranging habitat ensures that while one population may be struggling, another is surviving.

Black panther, a melanistic form of leopard

Leopards are excellent hunters. When hunting, leopards seldom rely on an **accomplice** from their own species to bring down their prey, since the animal is an **incorrigible** hermit that prefers a solitary existence. The leopard's jaw muscles are so powerful that it can catch and kill animals larger than itself. After a stealthy stalk, a leopard will charge at speeds of up to 35 miles per hour to catch its prey. Its remarkable strength **facilitates** its ability to carry quarry three times its size into trees. This practice protects the food from scavengers. Leopards prefer to stalk their prey when the **opaque** shadows of the night allow them to remain hidden hunters, but the animals also **brazenly** hunt during the day. This flexibility allows for a wider-ranging diet and increased hunting opportunities—another example of the species' unique ability to survive.

Humans also have had a hand in the rise and fall of leopard populations though. Leopards faced a serious threat from the fashion industry in the mid-20th century. Jacqueline Kennedy's appearance in a leopard-skin coat in 1964 served as a **catalyst**, leading to the rising popularity of the fur. Demand for leopard skins almost **annihilated** wild populations. A **militant** and ultimately successful campaign in the 1960s and 1970s opposing the use of leopard skins as fashion items is another reason that this animal's populations are now thriving.

While some subspecies of leopards have **stagnant** population growth or are even close to extinction, such as the Amur Leopard of Russia, the species population worldwide is impressive. According to current estimates by international conservation groups, it is highly unlikely that wild leopards will **succumb** to extinction any time soon.

Audio

For iWords and audio passages, go to SadlierConnect.com.

Left: African leopard;
Above: Indian snow leopard

Definitions

Note the spelling, pronunciation, part(s) of speech, and definition(s) of each of the following words. Then write the appropriate form of the word in the blank space in the illustrative sentence(s) following.

1. **arbitrary**
(är' bə trer ē)

   (*adj.*) unreasonable; based on one's wishes or whims without regard for reason or fairness

   A judge may be criticized for rulings that appear to be _____ and without legal precedent.

2. **catalyst**
(kat' əl ist)

   (*n.*) a substance that causes or hastens a chemical reaction; any agent that causes change

   Enzymes are _____ that aid in the digestion of food.

3. **facilitate**
(fə sil' ə tāt)

   (*v.*) to make easier; to assist

   The Federal Reserve Board may lower interest rates in order to _____ economic growth.

4. **incorrigible**
(in kä' rə jə bəl)

   (*adj.*) not able to be corrected; beyond control

   Criminals deemed _____ can expect to receive maximum sentences for their offenses against society.

5. **militant**
(mil' ə tənt)

   (*adj.*) given to fighting; active and aggressive in support of a cause; (*n.*) an activist

   In the struggle for civil rights, Martin Luther King, Jr., advocated peaceful rather than _____ protest.

   Elizabeth Cady Stanton was a _____ in the fight for woman suffrage.

6. **paramount**
(par' ə maunt)

   (*adj.*) chief in importance, above all others

   Voters should insist that candidates for high office address the _____ issues facing our society.

7. **rebut**
(ri bət')

   (*v.*) to offer arguments or evidence that contradict an assertion; to refute

   It is a defense lawyer's job to _____ the charges made by the prosecutor.

8. **reprimand**
(rep' rə mand)

   (*v.*) to scold; find fault with; (*n.*) a rebuke

   A judge may need to _____ a lawyer for repeatedly harassing a witness.

   An employee who frequently violates a company's rules may receive a written _____.

9. **servitude**
(sər' və tüd)

(n.) slavery, forced labor
In *Les Misérables*, Jean Valjean is sentenced to many years of _____ for stealing a loaf of bread.

10. **slapdash**
(slap' dash)

(adj.) careless and hasty
Landlords who routinely make _____ repairs should be considered negligent.

Using Context

*For each item, determine whether the **boldface** word from pages 70–71 makes sense in the context of the sentence. Circle the item numbers next to the six sentences in which the words are used correctly.*

1. We don't have much information to go on, so we will have to make an **arbitrary** decision about which house painter to hire.

2. The crew of workers will immediately **rebut** the walls of the crumbling building to prevent a collapse.

3. Seeing slavery firsthand was such a **catalyst** in young Abraham Lincoln's life that he developed a deep, lifelong opposition to it.

4. No matter how important the event or how many people she keeps waiting, my **incorrigible** cousin always manages to arrive late.

5. Critics agreed that the collection of essays was a fitting and **slapdash** tribute to Mark Twain and well worth reading.

6. Bad habits, such as not getting enough sleep or putting off studying until the last minute, **facilitate** learning.

7. Because both sides in the dispute were so **militant**, they easily reached an agreement.

8. The defendant was lucky to receive a **reprimand** rather than a jail sentence from the judge.

9. Of all the natural wonders to see in the United States, I believe that the Grand Canyon in Arizona and Niagara Falls in New York are **paramount**.

10. In the famous fairy tale, Cinderella lives a life of **servitude**, while her selfish stepsisters, by contrast, enjoy a life of luxury and privilege.

Choosing the Right Word

*Select the **boldface** word that better completes each sentence. You might refer to the passage on pages 68–69 to see how most of these words are used in context. Note that the choices might be related forms of the Unit words.*

1. Most historians agree that military disasters during World War I were the (**militants, catalyst**) that sparked the Russian Revolution of 1917.

2. The best way to (**facilitate, rebut**) the contention that something is not possible to do is to go out and do it.

3. (**Reprimands, Militants**), disgusted with the government's policies, took to the streets to register a vote of no confidence.

4. People who never give any assignment more than a "lick and a promise" may be said to belong to the (**incorrigible, slapdash**) school of working.

5. For the world's starving millions, finding enough food to keep body and soul together has become the (**paramount, slapdash**) concern in life.

6. The boss's (**servitude, reprimand**) stung his employee especially hard, as it was delivered in front of the entire staff.

7. Since they are firmly based on the logic of a sentence, the rules of punctuation should not be considered purely (**arbitrary, slapdash**).

8. Her excellent command of both French and Spanish should (**reprimand, facilitate**) her efforts to get a position in the foreign service.

9. The family's (**servitude, catalyst**) to the local lords had begun generations earlier, when an ancestor's misfortunes had resulted in a loss of wealth and status.

10. He has deceived me so many times that I am forced to conclude that he is simply a(n) (**incorrigible, arbitrary**) liar.

11. On rare occasions, the U.S. Senate will (**reprimand, facilitate**) one of its members who has violated the rules.

12. Even people who appear to be free may be in (**catalyst, servitude**) to their own passions and prejudices.

Completing
the Sentence

Choose the word from the word bank that best completes each of the following sentences. Write the correct word or form of the word in the space provided.

arbitrary	facilitate	militant	rebut	servitude
catalyst	incorrigible	paramount	reprimand	slapdash

1. The fact that you cannot control those small children does not mean that they are_____.

2. The helpful librarian did much to _____ the research for my term paper.

3. Many people came to the Americas after they had been sentenced to terms of penal _____ for crimes they had committed.

4. Mom and Dad said nothing when I failed the examination, but the disappointed looks on their faces hurt more than the most severe _____.

5. In guaranteeing the right to "due process of law," the Constitution protects Americans against _____ arrest and imprisonment.

6. In certain industrial processes, _____ speed up the desired reaction by lessening the amount of energy needed to produce it.

7. It is an unfortunate fact that the _____ attitudes of Germany's kaiser and his saber-rattling cronies helped make World War I inevitable.

8. "If you spent more time and effort on your essays, they would cease to be such _____ affairs," my older sister priggishly observed.

9. No matter what make of automobile you have, it is of _____ importance that you learn to drive safely before you use it.

10. After both of the opposing speakers had presented their cases, they were allowed time to _____ each other's arguments.

Definitions

Note the spelling, pronunciation, part(s) of speech, and definition(s) of each of the following words. Then write the appropriate form of the word in the blank space in the illustrative sentence(s) following.

1. **accomplice**
   (ə käm′ plis)

   (*n.*) a person who takes part in a crime
   The driver of the getaway car was arrested and tried as an_____ in the daring bank robbery.

2. **annihilate**
   (ə nī′ ə lāt)

   (*v.*) to destroy completely
   Throughout history, nations that are bitter enemies have sought to _____ each other.

3. **brazen**
   (brā′ zən)

   (*adj.*) shameless, impudent; made of brass
   Behavior considered _____ in one era may be deemed perfectly acceptable in another.

4. **exodus**
   (ek′ sə dəs)

   (*n.*) a large-scale departure or flight
   The _____ of African Americans to the industrialized northern states is known as the Great Migration.

5. **latent**
   (lāt′ ənt)

   (*adj.*) hidden, present but not realized
   Don't you think it's sad that many people use only a small fraction of their _____ abilities?

6. **morose**
   (mə rōs′)

   (*adj.*) having a gloomy or sullen manner; not friendly or sociable
   Heathcliff is the _____ and vengeful protagonist in Emily Brontë's novel *Wuthering Heights*.

7. **opaque**
   (ō pāk′)

   (*adj.*) not letting light through; not clear or lucid; dense, stupid
   I have read that book twice, but I still find the author's meaning completely _____.

8. **prattle**
   (prat′ əl)

   (*v.*) to talk in an aimless, foolish, or simple way; to babble;
   (*n.*) baby talk; babble
   Some people can _____ away on the phone for hours on end.
   Over time, recognizable words become part of a toddler's cheerful _____.

| 9. **stagnant**
(stag′ nənt) | (*adj.*) not running or flowing; foul from standing still; inactive
It is dangerous for hikers to drink water from any source that appears to be _____. |
| 10. **succumb**
(sə kəm′) | (*v.*) to give way to superior force, yield
Most dieters occasionally _____ to the lure of a high-calorie dessert. |

Using Context

*For each item, determine whether the **boldface** word from pages 74–75 makes sense in the context of the sentence. Circle the item numbers next to the six sentences in which the words are used correctly.*

1. The salesman tried to sell me a more expensive wireless networking plan, but I refused to **succumb** to his efforts and bought only the basic service.

2. The **prattle** of the clock tower's bells is useful for knowing the time but disruptive when trying to sleep.

3. No one saw the thief's face, but a few witnesses gave a detailed description of the vehicle belonging to the **accomplice**.

4. People were worried that the storm would **annihilate** the town, but it passed through without causing much damage.

5. The **latent** sound of the birds chirping as we waited for the bus lifted our spirits.

6. Despite losing the game, the **morose** basketball players congratulated the opposing team.

7. Since I was too busy to eat all day, I felt relieved to arrive home to the **opaque** smell of dinner in the oven.

8. Some summer afternoons, the air feels so **stagnant** that I even miss the harsh winds of winter.

9. She was thrilled to receive an A on the test but acted in a **brazen** manner so that she would not be accused of bragging.

10. The **exodus** of city-dwellers during the summer can make the normally crowded streets seem eerily quiet.

Choosing the Right Word

*Select the **boldface** word that better completes each sentence. You might refer to the passage on pages 68–69 to see how most of these words are used in context. Note that the choices might be related forms of the Unit words.*

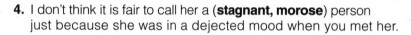

1. The brook (**prattling, annihilating**) along its rocky course seemed to be conversing wordlessly with the wind murmuring in the trees.

2. It is up to us to get rid of any (**latent, morose**) prejudices that we may still unwittingly hold against members of other races and nationalities.

3. While his (**accomplices, prattles**) acted as decoys, one of the youngsters attempted to filch a couple of apples from the unguarded bin.

4. I don't think it is fair to call her a (**stagnant, morose**) person just because she was in a dejected mood when you met her.

5. With their bigger, faster, more experienced players, South High simply (**succumbed, annihilated**) our team, 56 to 7.

6. You may think that his explanation is perfectly clear, but I find it confused and (**brazen, opaque**).

7. During the summer, urban "sun worshippers" begin their weekly (**exodus, prattle**) from the city at around 3:00 p.m. on Friday.

8. Unemployment will stay at a high level so long as a nation's economy remains (**stagnant, brazen**).

9. I refuse to believe that our society will (**annihilate, succumb**) to the weaknesses that have destroyed other nations.

10. The leaden silence of the afternoon was shattered by the (**opaque, brazen**) voices of trumpets braying fanfares for the returning hero.

11. I worried that the toddler's (**exodus, prattle**) would continue throughout the film.

12. Her (**stagnant, brazen**) demeanor might help her to be a successful salesperson, but it could also alienate potential customers.

Completing the Sentence

Choose the word from the word bank that best completes each of the following sentences. Write the correct word or form of the word in the space provided.

accomplice	**brazen**	**latent**	**opaque**	**stagnant**
annihilate	**exodus**	**morose**	**prattle**	**succumb**

1. In large areas of the huge swamp, there were _____ pools of water covered with unmoving masses of green slime.

2. The doctor warned relatives that if the patient's condition deteriorated any further, she would _____ to pneumonia.

3. Fighting is considered such a(n) _____ violation of the rules of a game that the offending players are usually severely penalized.

4. If we are going to use this space as a darkroom for photography, we must have a completely _____ covering over the window.

5. His friends call him "Motormouth" because he has a remarkable capacity to _____ endlessly about the most trivial matters.

6. The second book of the Old Testament is named for the story it recounts of the _____ of the Israelites from the land of Egypt.

7. When she was suddenly deprived of everything she valued in life, the poor woman became extremely gloomy and _____.

8. The youth did not actually steal the car, but he was a(n) _____.

9. It is a frightening fact of modern life that we now possess the weaponry to _____ not only our enemies but all humankind.

10. Though she had always loved art, Grandma Moses did not discover her own _____ artistic talents until well into her seventies.

Synonyms

*Choose the word or form of the word from this Unit that is the same or most nearly the same in meaning as the **boldface** word or expression in the phrase. Write that word on the line. Use a dictionary if necessary.*

1. the **emigration** of refugees from the war zone   _____

2. refused to accept such **sloppy** work   _____

3. **aid** communication between two countries   _____

4. **bold** behavior   _____

5. **demolished** our rivals in the playoffs   _____

6. the **foremost** authority on the subject   _____

7. searched for the forger's **confederates**   _____

8. an **unashamed** gossip   _____

9. **chastised** them for their discourteous behavior   _____

10. **yield** to peer pressure   _____

11. a moving account of life in **captivity**   _____

12. a **stimulus** for change   _____

13. a **sullen** stare   _____

14. a **fetid** pond clogged with debris   _____

15. **chattered** about nothing in particular   _____

Antonyms

*Choose the word or form of the word from this Unit that is most nearly opposite in meaning to the **boldface** word or expression in the phrase. Write that word on the line. Use a dictionary if necessary.*

1. **confirm** the witness's testimony   _____

2. a piece of **transparent** cloth   _____

3. a **rational** decision   _____

4. a supporter with a **peaceable** attitude   _____

5. has **obvious** flu symptoms   _____

Writing: Words in Action

Write a short persuasive essay in which you try to convince an audience that one of the leopard's survival techniques most accounts for the animal's continued survival in the 21st century. Use at least two details from the passage (pages 68–69) and three or more words from this Unit to support your argument.

Vocabulary in Context

*Some of the words you have studied in this Unit appear in **boldface** type. Read the passage below, and then circle the letter of the correct answer for each word as it is used in context.*

In the wild, big cats such as leopards, tigers, and lions are mostly nocturnal. While lions live in relatively open habitats, leopards and tigers prefer dense jungle. Counting these species poses unique challenges to wildlife managers. However, due to technological advances, they have not yet become **morose** about the prospects for success.

Until recently, the census of big cats depended on pug marks: the paw impressions of tigers and leopards. It was thought that these paw prints were like human fingerprints, unique to every individual. However, wildlife experts eventually condemned this census technique as **slapdash.** They claimed there were too many chances for human error in the tracing and **arbitrary** analysis of pug marks. Census figures, in these experts' views, were childish **prattle**, often inflated by a forest officer's ambition for promotion. Biologists **reprimanded** the forest authorities, spurring them on to adopt more modern methods.

Servitude to the pug mark technique, though, was slow to die. At length, with the development of camera trap techniques, big cats that crossed an infrared beam at carefully chosen locations triggered cameras mounted on posts; tigers and leopards, in effect, took "selfies." This allowed officials to carefully compare the facial markings and side stripes of tigers. These patterns, unique to each individual, offer a far more reliable means of identification than pug marks.

In another advance, counting the elusive felines now involves DNA analysis of droppings. Collecting scat on forest trails may be an unpleasant task, but DNA determinations may offer the most reliable evidence of all on the status of wild cat populations. In the case of top predators, like tigers, knowing their population numbers helps researchers determine the long-term health of protected areas.

---

1. If you are **morose**, you are
   a. optimistic   c. gloomy
   b. blithe   d. jaunty

2. A method that is **slapdash** might also be described as
   a. painstaking   c. aggressive
   b. costly   d. careless

3. If an analysis is **arbitrary,** it is
   a. random   c. judgmental
   b. coherent   d. equitable

4. The word **prattle** most nearly means
   a. imagery   c. folk tales
   b. babble   d. ghost stories

5. People who are **reprimanded** are
   a. complimented   c. scolded
   b. advised   d. fired

6. **Servitude** means a state of
   a. well-being   c. elation
   b. bondage   d. doubt

*Read the following passage, taking note of the **boldface** words and their contexts. These words are among those you will be studying in Unit 6. It may help you to complete the exercises in this Unit if you refer to the way the words are used below.*

Modernize the School Calendar
<Persuasive Essay>

"**S**hould the school day be longer?" "Should administrators lengthen the school year?" Some people would answer both questions with "No." Insisting that students already work **incessantly** during the day, they argue that students need those after-school hours and summer days to earn money, help at home, or pursue key interests. Supporters of the current school year argue that keeping schools open later and longer will cost too much. Such advocates **hew** to the argument that school time need not be longer, just better spent. Those contentions are **lucid** and **credible**—anyone can see that. But for the sake of the students' futures, the answer to both questions must be "Yes."

The current school year in the United States is a product of 19th-century thinking. School schedules were shaped by the harsh demands of city life or were in **bondage** to the unyielding hold of farm life. In rural areas, children had to be available for spring planting and fall harvesting. Thus, they customarily were in school only from December to March and from mid-May through August. But as the population of the urban United States ballooned, the educational experts of the day shifted their attention to city schools. Prominent educators, Horace Mann among them,

One-room schoolhouses were abundant in the 20th century.

A typical urban class in 1914 did not meet during the heat of the summer.

Students in South Korea meet 220 days a year.

believed that students needed a long break to avoid overstimulation. Physicians worried that students would suffer nervous disorders from work pressures. Doctors predicted illnesses caused by the heat of the classrooms in summer. These concerns resulted in the two-month summer holiday, and even though there is nothing permanent about such a long break, belief in adherence to the 180-day school year retains its **tenacious** hold on the thinking of many educators. These apprehensions are **superfluous** today.

How can the United States stay competitive in the global economy when so many of its students' international peers are in classrooms for more days and longer days? In fact, Japanese students have a 243-day school year, and South Korean students are in school for 220 days a year. Despite the **diligence** of our hardworking teachers and the high quality of our educational institutions, our students are struggling to keep pace, **hampered** by a 20th-century school schedule that holds back the 21st-century student. The argument that the expense of keeping schools open longer would **impoverish** school districts is easily refuted. First of all, buildings kept open later can serve other vital community needs and be rented to

civic groups. Secondly, the costs would be **defrayed** by the improved skills students would bring to medicine, science, and business. Horace Mann might **posthumously** agree that modern conveniences make schools comfortable year round.

Many today see the writing on the wall. They understand that having hardworking and caring educators as well as fresh, thoughtful curricula are not enough to **atone** for the short school year. In March 2009, President Obama spoke of the **intricacies** of the issue. He stated that in order to compete favorably with their international peers, students in the U.S. need to spend more time in school. To guarantee a brighter future for the country it is necessary to **supplant** the current school schedule with a modern one.

Audio

For iWords and audio passages, go to SadlierConnect.com.

Definitions

Note the spelling, pronunciation, part(s) of speech, and definition(s) of each of the following words. Then write the appropriate form of the word in the blank space in the illustrative sentence(s) following.

1. atone
(ə tōn')

(*v.*) to make up for
At one time or another, everyone has done something for which he or she needs to _____.

2. credible
(kred' ə bəl)

(*adj.*) believable
Do you have a _____ explanation for not completing your assignment on time?

3. doleful
(dōl' fəl)

(*adj.*) sad; dreary
One look at the players' _____ faces told me that the team had lost the championship game.

4. hamper
(ham' pər)

(*v.*) to hold back
Poor grades will _____ you in your effort to get a college education.

5. impoverished
(im päv' risht)

(*adj.*) poor, in a state of poverty; depleted
After World War II, _____ European countries received U.S. aid under the Marshall Plan.

6. lucid
(lü' sid)

(*adj.*) easy to understand, clear; rational, sane
The ability to speak in a _____ and persuasive fashion is a great asset to a politician.

7. posthumous
(päs' chə məs)

(*adj.*) occurring or published after death
Many artists and writers have been ignored during their lifetimes only to achieve _____ fame.

8. sardonic
(sär dän' ik)

(*adj.*) grimly or scornfully mocking, bitterly sarcastic
Great satirists save their most _____ wit for the greedy, the corrupt, and the hypocritical.

9. supplant
(sə plant')

(v.) to take the place of, supersede

Computers rapidly _____ typewriters in the workplace, just as photocopiers replaced carbon paper.

10. tenacious
(tə nā' shəs)

(adj.) holding fast; holding together firmly; persistent

Athletes must be _____ in the pursuit of excellence if they hope to become Olympic champions.

Using Context

*For each item, determine whether the **boldface** word from pages 82–83 makes sense in the context of the sentence. Circle the item numbers next to the six sentences in which the words are used correctly.*

1. The jazz composer who died in 2011 received a **posthumous** special award last year.

2. The doctor established herself as a highly **credible** witness when she told the jury that she had twenty years of experience as a medical examiner.

3. My dog's naturally **doleful** expression makes him look sad even when he is perfectly content.

4. The summer camp provided twice-daily swimming lessons to the children to **hamper** their ability to swim.

5. Fortunately, my aunt has been able to **supplant** her business by advertising its services on social media networks.

6. The **impoverished** neighborhood was filled with fancy shops, luxury cars, and expensive restaurants.

7. In the famous tale by Dickens, it is a vision of his future that finally causes Ebenezer Scrooge to turn his life around and **atone** for his unkind treatment of others.

8. It's hard to imagine that anyone could ever comprehend or believe that **lucid** explanation.

9. W.C. Fields was one early movie star who was known for his clever remarks and **sardonic** wit.

10. The **tenacious** detective was able to solve the cold case fifteen years after the crime had been committed.

Choosing the Right Word

*Select the **boldface** word that better completes each sentence. You might refer to the passage on pages 80–81 to see how most of these words are used in context. Note that the choices might be related forms of the Unit words.*

1. If we were to lose the basic freedoms guaranteed by the Bill of Rights, we would be truly (**lucid, impoverished**).

2. "The witness has changed her story so often that no jury on earth is likely to find her testimony (**tenacious, credible**)," the district attorney observed.

3. The author's writing style is as (**lucid, sardonic**) as the sparkling waters of a mountain lake on a spring morning.

4. I refuse to (**supplant, atone**) for something that I still believe was the right thing to do, even if no one else agrees with me.

5. Royalties from a novel that is published (**credibly, posthumously**) normally go to the author's estate.

6. (**Hampered, Impoverished**) by the weight of my backpack, I took longer to reach the bus stop.

7. The novel's grim humor and (**posthumous, sardonic**) portrayal of the futility of all human endeavor make it an intensely disturbing book.

8. Once she adopted the puppy, her enjoyment of the new pet began to (**supplant, hamper**) the sadness she felt over the death of the dog she'd had since childhood.

9. Frankly, I am tired of your endless (**credible, doleful**) complaints about all the people who have been unfair to you.

10. I know that love is fickle, but I never expected to be (**atoned, supplanted**) in her affections by a man like that.

11. He is very slow to form opinions; but once he does, he holds on to them (**tenaciously, dolefully**).

12. In some early societies, people who had committed certain crimes could (**atone, hamper**) for them by paying sums of money to their victims.

Completing the Sentence

Choose the word from the word bank that best completes each of the following sentences. Write the correct word or form of the word in the space provided.

atone	doleful	impoverished	posthumous	supplant
credible	hamper	lucid	sardonic	tenacious

1. When the stock market collapsed in 1929, many wealthy speculators found themselves as _____ as proverbial church mice.

2. Saying "I'm sorry" is a good way to begin to _____ for the suffering or harm that you have done to another person.

3. I know that he will say anything to save his own skin, but I feel that in this case his account of the incident is _____ and should be accepted.

4. I suppose bloodhounds may be as happy as other dogs, but they have the _____ look of creatures who have lost their last friend.

5. Although the survivors were still in a state of shock, some of them were _____ enough to answer the questions posed by the police.

6. During World War II, artificial rubber began to _____ natural rubber in American automobile tires.

7. On the steps of the Capitol, the president awarded _____ Medals of Honor to soldiers who had recently fallen in defense of the country.

8. "Someone with such a(n) _____ grip on life doesn't give up the ghost easily," I thought as I watched the old woman celebrate another birthday.

9. The huge piles of snow that cover the roads will greatly _____ the efforts of the rescue team to reach the stranded skiers.

10. The wily old senator derived a certain amount of _____ amusement from watching his enemies turn on and destroy one another.

Definitions

Note the spelling, pronunciation, part(s) of speech, and definition(s) of each of the following words. Then write the appropriate form of the word in the blank space in the illustrative sentence(s) following.

1. bondage
(bän′ dij)

(*n.*) slavery; any state of being bound or held down

Many people escaped the cruel _____ of slavery with the help of the Underground Railroad.

2. defray
(dē frā′)

(*v.*) to pay for

Corporate sponsors helped to _____ the cost of the charity's annual telethon.

3. diligent
(dil′ ə jənt)

(*adj.*) hardworking, industrious, not lazy

_____ employees are likely to be well rewarded for their dedication and hard work.

4. ghastly
(gast′ lē)

(*adj.*) frightful, horrible; deathly pale

Some people are almost afraid to go to sleep because they suffer from _____ recurring nightmares.

5. hew
(hyü)

(*v.*) to shape or cut down with an ax; to hold to

Even in a crisis, we must _____ to this nation's principles of liberty, equality, and justice.

6. incessant
(in ses′ ənt)

(*adj.*) never stopping, going on all the time

The loud and _____ chatter of the people at the next table made it hard for us to hear each other.

7. intricate
(in′ trə kət)

(*adj.*) complicated; difficult to understand

Our teacher took us through the _____ solution to the equation step by step.

8. prim
(prim)

(*adj.*) overly neat, proper, or formal; prudish

How is it that such a _____ and tidy person and such a messy one can be such good friends?

9. **superfluous**
(sü par' flü was)

(*adj.*) exceeding what is sufficient or required, excess
Neat and well-organized people know how to eliminate all _____ clutter.

10. **taunt**
(tônt)

(*v.*) to jeer at, mock; (*n.*) an insulting or mocking remark
It is not at all unusual for brothers and sisters to tease and _____ one another good-naturedly.

For umpires and referees, the _____ of angry fans are just part of the job.

Using Context

*For each item, determine whether the **boldface** word from pages 86–87 makes sense in the context of the sentence. Circle the item numbers next to the six sentences in which the words are used correctly.*

1. The entire audience was enchanted by the lead singer's **superfluous** voice.

2. I was nervous about giving my presentation to the class until hearing an encouraging **taunt** from my friend.

3. My cousin and I are only in **incessant** contact, but when we are able to talk, it's as if no time has passed.

4. Until my father found the courage to follow his dreams and start his own business, he was held in **bondage** by his own fears and doubts.

5. Although I sometimes find it restricting, I always **hew** to the curfew set by my parents.

6. The two job candidates left such contrasting impressions; one seemed **prim** and reserved, whereas the other was casual and chatty.

7. Understanding math does not come easily to him, but because he is a **diligent** student he earned an A in the class.

8. On a hot summer day, there are few things more satisfying than jumping into the **ghastly** waters of a lake.

9. Only a skilled technician can reassemble the **intricate** circuits and complex components of this device.

10. The profits from the fundraiser will go directly to the fund that helps the school **defray** the cost of the auditorium refurbishment.

Choosing the Right Word

Select the **boldface** word that better completes each sentence. You might refer to the passage on pages 80–81 to see how most of these words are used in context. Note that the choices might be related forms of the Unit words.

1. The trophy was completely (**incessant, superfluous**), as the pleasure of winning was all that mattered to her.

2. In a totalitarian state, people who do not (**hew, defray**) firmly to the party line are likely to find themselves in hot water with the authorities.

3. Even after the most systematic and (**ghastly, diligent**) search, we could not find the missing documents.

4. If we want government to provide services, we must pay taxes to (**defray, taunt**) the costs.

5. His feverish and (**prim, incessant**) activity cannot hide the fact that he doesn't know what he's doing.

6. She could never quite forget her sister's hurtful childhood (**bondage, taunts**).

7. That village is famous all over the world for its demure cottages, well-manicured lawns, and (**prim, diligent**) gardens.

8. "Sticks and stones may break my bones, but names will never hurt me" is an old saying I try to keep in mind whenever someone (**hews, taunts**) me.

9. When I looked through the microscope, I observed the (**incessant, intricate**) pattern of blood vessels in the specimen's body.

10. Loss of blood very quickly turned the victim's normally rosy face a (**prim, ghastly**) hue of white.

11. The details of the peace accord among the four nations, worked out by a host of foreign affairs officials over a period of months, were (**superfluous, intricate**).

12. What real use is financial independence if a person remains forever in (**bondage, taunt**) to foolish fears and superstitions?

Completing the Sentence

Choose the word from the word bank that best completes each of the following sentences. Write the correct word or form of the word in the space provided.

bondage	diligent	hew	intricate	superfluous
defray	ghastly	incessant	prim	taunt

1. He is a rather _____ sort of man who is easily shocked by other people's less exacting standards of conduct.

2. A student who is _____ and systematic in study habits will often do better than one who is brilliant but lazy.

3. "Since their heroic deeds clearly speak for themselves," the president remarked, "further comment on my part would be _____."

4. Our football team would do a great deal better if we mastered a few simple plays, instead of trying to use all those _____ formations.

5. Because my home is located at a busy intersection, I have been forced to accustom myself to the _____ hum of traffic outside.

6. For thousands of years Native Americans used stone implements to _____ canoes out of logs and tree trunks.

7. A woman of strong character and noble bearing, she endured the jibes and _____ of her adversaries with great patience and fortitude.

8. Lincoln said: "Familiarize yourself with the chains of _____ and you prepare your own limbs to wear them."

9. To help _____ the expenses that I would incur on the senior class trip to Washington, I worked as a babysitter.

10. I shall never forget the _____ sight that greeted us when we arrived at the scene of the incident.

Synonyms

*Choose the word or form of the word from this Unit that is the same or most nearly the same in meaning as the **boldface** word or expression in the phrase. Write that word on the line. Use a dictionary if necessary.*

1. **complex** and beautiful designs _____

2. a **dogged** politician intent on winning _____

3. a target of the writer's **caustic** criticism _____

4. averted my eyes from the **gruesome** scene _____

5. **chop** wood for the fireplace _____

6. freed the hostage from **captivity** _____

7. **impede** the progress of the investigation _____

8. a **postmortem** analysis of the patient's condition _____

9. **made amends** for their misdeeds _____

10. refuses to respond to **derision** _____

11. a **prudish** way of dress _____

12. **replace** the abacus with the calculator _____

13. students **tireless** in their studies _____

14. writes **melancholy** songs about lost love _____

15. a fund to **settle** the cost of room and board _____

Antonyms

*Choose the word or form of the word from this Unit that is most nearly opposite in meaning to the **boldface** word or expression in the phrase. Write that word on the line. Use a dictionary if necessary.*

1. an **unintelligible** description of the accident _____

2. the **occasional** swaying of the ship in the storm _____

3. an **affluent** neighborhood _____

4. a story that is not **plausible** _____

5. the **essential** remarks in the speech _____

Writing: Words in Action

Which of the author's arguments in favor of a year-round school calendar do you believe is the strongest? Write a persuasive essay explaining the single best reason for extending students' time in school. Use at least two details from the passage (pages 80–81) and three or more words from the Unit to support your argument.

Vocabulary in Context

*Some of the words you have studied in this Unit appear in **boldface** type. Read the passage below, and then circle the letter of the correct answer for each word as it is used in context.*

Homework may seem like something that has always been a part of education, but it is actually an invention of the nineteenth century. In the 1800s before school became mandatory for children at specific ages, many students left school by fifth grade to financially support their **impoverished** families. For the few students who continued on to middle and high schools, the curriculum included drilling, recitation, and memorization. This **doleful** work required two to three hours of preparation at home each night. This amount of homework may not seem **ghastly**, but it often competed with the students' earning money for their families.

In the early twentieth century, the progressive education movement began to question whether recitation, drilling, and memorization were effective in educating students. When this concept came under scrutiny, so did the idea of homework. Pediatricians suggested that extended time playing outdoors would be more beneficial for children than completing assignments in **prim** handwriting. In 1900, the editor of a respected magazine wrote anti-homework articles that were read widely. Other individuals and organizations delivered their own anti-homework **taunts** until the 1940s, resulting in many school districts eliminating homework in elementary and middle schools. After the Russian launch of *Sputnik 1* in 1957, American leaders and educators viewed homework as a way for American children to compete globally.

These days, homework is still a noteworthy topic. While 21st-century students make **sardonic** remarks about the excessive amount of homework that they are given, educators and policy leaders theorize about the best way to educate today's students. The debate about the role of homework in learning will continue for years to come.

---

1. An **impoverished** family is
   a. poor
   b. resourceful
   c. young
   d. strict

2. Something that is **doleful**, as homework is said to be, is usually
   a. exhilarating
   b. quick
   c. dreary
   d. beneficial

3. The word **ghastly** most nearly means
   a. unknown
   b. horrible
   c. unique
   d. manageable

4. **Prim** handwriting can best be described as
   a. barely readable
   b. overly neat
   c. unusually small
   d. carelessly scribbled

5. A **taunt** is
   a. a theory
   b. an insult
   c. a compliment
   d. a prepared speech

6. **Sardonic** remarks are
   a. carefully prepared
   b. hurriedly written
   c. scornfully mocking
   d. formally composed

Vocabulary for Comprehension

Part 1

*Read this passage, which contains words in **boldface** that appear in Units 4–6. Then choose the best answer to each question based on what is stated or implied in the passage. You may refer to the passage as often as necessary.*

Questions 1–10 are based on the following passage.

For at least three decades, debate has intensified about the position and value of the humanities in American education. The humanities are typically defined as
(5) the fields of English, foreign languages, art and architecture, film and theater, music, philosophy, religion, and history. The percentage of undergraduate degrees awarded in these disciplines
(10) has been steadily declining. So has the number of doctoral degrees. Analysts of this shifting landscape have pointed to the increasing preoccupation, in education and society as a whole, with economic
(15) growth. The humanities, it is said, are viewed as "soft" subjects. They are **opaque** frills that do not translate readily into jobs—or even as subjective, self-indulgent areas of learning. It is troubling
(20) for some educators that the humanities seem **fated** to become an outdated educational novelty.

Pushback from **intrepid** humanists has not been slow in coming. Perhaps the most
(25) persuasive argument for the value of the humanities focuses on the cultivation of critical thinking. Literature, art, philosophy, and history are all disciplines that compel students to weigh alternatives, construct
(30) arguments, evaluate ethical choices, and critique analyses in ways that are unlike the requirements of the social and natural sciences. These disciplines, moreover, are closely linked to the long liberal arts
(35) **prototype** in American higher education. This approach was championed by such leading lights as Horace Mann and John Dewey. As recently as the 1970s, America's

elite institutions of higher learning promoted
(40) the humanities as a proving ground for prospective doctors, lawyers, and businesspeople. Graduate school was the arena for acquiring professional knowledge and skills. The undergraduate years, by
(45) contrast, outfitted young people with a well-rounded, culturally literate grounding.

In the recent debates, humanists have also emphasized that their disciplines **facilitate** the formation of democratic
(50) and world citizens. More than ever in a globalized world, advocates claim, young adults should be able to perceive the **intricate** interrelationships between different cultures. They should be able to
(55) envision themselves in the shoes of others who are very different. To this end, the study of literature, history, and world religions may be expected to make vital contributions. Humanists readily grant that
(60) their advocacy is in no way intended to denigrate the contributions of "harder" sciences such as economics. But they insist that the engagement of imagination and empathy that humanities disciplines
(65) typically call forth provides a **paramount** facet of contemporary education.

Finally, arguments highlighting the value of the humanities include the **lucid** contention that these subjects collectively
(70) form a "good in itself," irrespective of any tangible benefit. Why do we bother to attend a performance of *Hamlet?* What good comes from listening to a Beethoven quartet? What benefit do we derive from
(75) delving into another culture's mythology? A **tenacious** "good in itself" answer to these questions parallels, to some degree, the "beauty of nature" axiom upheld by

environmentalists in their efforts to enlist
(80) support for conservation. Once an old-
growth forest is cut down, it can never
be restored, assert the preservationists.
Likewise, once cultural literacy disappears,
in humanist eyes, society is the poorer.

1. The primary purpose of the passage is to
   A) compare and contrast the humanities
   with the "hard" sciences.
   B) explicate the educational philosophy
   of Horace Mann and John Dewey.
   C) provide an overview of arguments
   promoting the value of the humanities.
   D) refute the allegation that the humanities
   are the victim of declining enrollments.

2. In can reasonably be inferred that the
   author refers to the preoccupation with
   economic growth (lines 13–15) in order to
   A) illustrate one cause of the declining
   popularity of humanities study.
   B) demonstrate the shortsightedness
   of those who prefer economic growth
   to the study of humanities.
   C) protest against the exaggerated
   importance of the study of economics.
   D) reflect ironically on the desire of
   most students to get a job in their
   fields of study.

3. As it is used in line 17, the word
   "opaque" most nearly means
   A) extravagant.
   B) transparent.
   C) optional.
   D) hazy.

4. In the second paragraph (lines 23–46),
   the author focuses on the connections
   between the humanities and
   A) graduate schools.
   B) critical thinking.
   C) ethical choices.
   D) the professions of law and medicine.

5. As it is used in line 35, the word
   "prototype" most nearly means
   A) model.
   B) symbol.
   C) summary.
   D) paraphrase.

6. Which of the following statements best
   captures the main idea of the third
   paragraph (lines 47–66)?
   A) Humanities disciplines engage the
   imagination and empathy of students.
   B) In an era of globalization, the humanities
   should be considered less important.
   C) The humanities prepare students
   effectively for citizenship.
   D) Economics may qualify to be
   considered one of the humanities.

7. Which choice provides the best evidence
   for the answer in the previous question?
   A) Lines 47–50 ("In the . . . citizens")
   B) Lines 50–55 ("More . . . others")
   C) Lines 56–59 ("To . . . contributions")
   D) Lines 59–62 ("Humanists . . . economics")

8. As it is used in line 65, "paramount"
   most nearly means
   A) parenthetical.
   B) ancillary.
   C) supreme.
   D) progressive.

9. The reference to the environment in lines
   78–82 is most likely intended to be a(n)
   A) metaphor.
   B) analogy.
   C) parable.
   D) allusion.

10. The overall tone of the passage may
   best be described as
   A) biased.
   B) melancholy.
   C) satirical.
   D) evenhanded.

Vocabulary for Comprehension
Part 2

*Read these passages, which contain words in **boldface** that appear in Units 4–6. Then choose the best answer to each question based on what is stated or implied in the passage(s). You may refer to the passages as often as necessary.*

Questions 1–10 are based on the following passages.

Passage 1

In ancient Greece, early drama probably emerged in the sixth century BCE from religious celebrations held in honor of gods and goddesses. Entertainment at
(5) these religious festivals likely included reenactments of a deity's best-known deeds, as well as choral songs and dances performed at banquets and other celebrations. Such songs were known as
(10) dithyrambs. It seems improbable that the choruses would **hew** to a set script or program. Rather, the tales and praises were likely drawn from the oral tradition and repeated from year to year with a substantial
(15) but **credible** dose of improvisation. Drama performed at Athens in the fifth century BCE was staged at civic festivals in honor of the god Dionysus. The chorus was an essential component of both tragedy and comedy.
(20) Ancient sources say the first person to tilt the balance decisively from choral performance to individual acting in drama was Thespis, a **catalyst** who won a prize for tragedy at Athens about 534 BCE.
(25) Except for a few references, however, history has **absconded** with most details of Thespis's achievement. We know that he recited a prologue and set speeches in his performances. He also disguised
(30) his face in various ways, including the use of a linen mask, to allow a way of acting the part of more than one character. In the following generation, Aeschylus—the first

Greek playwright whom we know firsthand
(35) from his surviving plays—introduced a second actor to dramatic performances. In the early fifth century BCE, comedy joined tragedy at the annual city festivals.

Passage 2

Oral tradition is the passing down,
(40) from one generation to the next, of stories, poems, historical lore, and other material by word of mouth. Within the past century, oral tradition has been recognized as a hugely important process in the development of
(45) countless cultures. There are still numerous societies which have not **succumbed** to the technology of writing.
 By the mid-1900s, it was widely accepted that Homer's monumental epics, the *Iliad*
(50) and the *Odyssey*, were the products of oral composition. **Diligent** scholars speculate that the epics were composed by one or more traditional oral bards. These singers of tales came at the end
(55) of a long line of poets skilled in both tradition and spontaneous innovation. This type of composition has often been compared to jazz improvisation.
 After the invention of the Greek
(60) alphabet, the Homeric epics were written down. Despite its **access** to written texts, however, ancient Greek society remained largely oral until the fourth century BCE. In the late 400s, the playwright Euripides
(65) was singled out as eccentric because he owned a library. In his dialogue the *Ion,* Plato paints a picture for us of a culture

that was still oral. Recitation artists known as rhapsodes would entertain audiences
(70) with oral performances of Homer. And in another dialogue, the *Phaedrus,* Socrates argues at length that written philosophy is **stagnant**. To be fully alive and valuable, philosophy must take its **arduous** yet
(75) rewarding shape from the spoken, rather than the written, word.

1. As it is used in line 11, "hew" most nearly means
   A) chop.
   B) hold to.
   C) correspond.
   D) shape.

2. In Passage 1, what is the main idea of the second paragraph (lines 20–38)?
   A) Thespis was the first recorded winner of a prize for tragedy at Athens.
   B) Aeschylus established himself as a finer tragedian than Thespis.
   C) Thespis was pivotal in the shift from choral performance to individual acting in drama.
   D) Thespis was a purely legendary figure, and no one knows much about him.

3. As it is used in line 26, "absconded" most nearly means
   A) run off and hidden.
   B) made clear and easy.
   C) obscured.
   D) duplicated.

4. As it is used in line 46, "succumbed" most nearly means
   A) apologized.
   B) conformed.
   C) dedicated.
   D) yielded.

5. The second paragraph of Passage 2 states that the *Iliad* and *Odyssey* are essentially
   A) folktales.
   B) historically inaccurate.
   C) oral compositions.
   D) religious rituals.

6. Which statement best describes the overall relationship between the passages?
   A) The objective of Passage 1 is to persuade, while the goal of Passage 2 is to inform.
   B) Passage 1 includes citations from early Greek drama, while Passage 2 omits any reference to Greek tragedy.
   C) Passage 1 focuses on religious rituals, while Passage 2 focuses on literature.
   D) Passage 1 covers the evolution of Greek drama, while Passage 2 discusses the importance of Greek oral tradition.

7. As it is used in line 73, "stagnant" most nearly means
   A) inactive.
   B) whimsical.
   C) erroneous.
   D) placid.

8. The author of Passage 2 would most likely conclude that the discussion of Thespis's achievements in Passage 1 (lines 27–32)
   A) was improbable, given the scantiness of the historical sources.
   B) supports the idea that Thespis's acting developed in an oral context.
   C) should have included a comparison of Thespis and Aeschylus.
   D) should have indicated if Thespis acted in both comedy and tragedy.

9. In Passage 1, the author emphasizes the role of oral tradition dithyrambs. In Passage 2, the author is more concerned with
   A) the persistence of the oral tradition in ancient Greece.
   B) the importance of the invention of the Greek alphabet.
   C) the personality of Socrates, as he was portrayed by Plato.
   D) the contributions of Euripides to ancient Greek tragedy.

10. Which choice provides the best evidence for the answer to the previous question?
   A) Lines 42–45 ("Within . . . cultures)
   B) Lines 54–56 ("These . . . innovation")
   C) Lines 61–63 ("Despite . . . BCE")
   D) Lines 68–70 ("Recitation . . . Homer")

Synonyms

*From the word bank below, choose the word that has the same or nearly the same meaning as the **boldface** word in each sentence and write it on the line. You will not use all of the words.*

anarchy	doleful	opaque	servitude
atone	inanimate	paramount	stagnant
auspicious	incessant	pompous	succumb
bondage	larceny	prattle	superfluous

1. His **sorrowful** expression is likely a result of a series of misfortunes that his family has suffered the last year. _____

2. I was hoping to have a meaningful conversation with my old friend, but instead I had to listen to her **babble** for hours. _____

3. The mayor's **dominant** concern is what to do about the growing numbers of homeless people in the city. _____

4. The teammates were bolstered by the **promising** start of the playoff game after they scored the first goal. _____

5. The film would have been better if it had not included **excess** scenes for comedic effect. _____

6. The **constant** drilling from the construction outside made what should have been a relaxing break quite stressful. _____

7. I feel that by doing volunteer work, I can **make up** for any greediness I may have displayed in the past. _____

8. The two employees were accused of **stealing** when they moved company funds into their private accounts. _____

9. I often find that I **yield** to my sister's requests for favors just to get her to stop pestering me. _____

10. The unpopular government understood that without tight control over its angry citizens, **chaos** would ensue. _____

11. He is the best student in the class, but I cannot deal with his **self-important** attitude for long enough to ask for help on the assignment. _____

12. The reasoning behind her argument is so **murky** that I don't even know where to begin in refuting her points. _____

Two-Word Completions

Select the pair of words that best completes the meaning of each of the following sentences.

1. His lies sounded so much like the truth that I was completely taken in by them. If they hadn't seemed so _____, I don't think I would have been _____ quite so easily.
   a. credible … hoodwinked
   b. ghastly … annihilated
   c. intricate … disentangled
   d. intrepid … impoverished

2. "I'm trying to help you, not _____ you," I said. "I want to make your task easier, not more _____."
   a. revile … pliant
   b. supplant … latent
   c. reprieve … slapdash
   d. hamper … arduous

3. "A(n) _____ is supposed to _____ the commission of a crime," the burglar growled at his sidekick. (The latter had just set off the alarm system to the bank the pair were robbing.) "But all *you* can seem to do," the burglar continued, "is make this job more difficult!"
   a. accomplice … facilitate
   b. rebuttal … incinerate
   c. precipice … reprimand
   d. catalyst … revile

4. Though learning a foreign language never comes easily for me, I've found that I can _____ the process if I imitate the ant in the old fable and apply myself to the task as _____ as possible.
   a. rectify … brazenly
   b. facilitate … diligently
   c. defray … credibly
   d. hamper … tenaciously

5. Tourists always gasp in amazement when _____ Mexican daredevils climb to the top of a lofty _____ in Acapulco and dive fearlessly into the sea hundreds of feet below.
   a. intrepid … precipice
   b. pliant … exodus
   c. brazen … access
   d. prim … catalyst

6. They could no longer sit idly by while a gross injustice went uncorrected. For that reason, they joined a group of _____ reformers actively trying to get the government to _____ the situation.
   a. incorrigible … disentangle
   b. militant … rectify
   c. morose … defray
   d. arbitrary … taunt

7. Shakespeare's Timon of Athens is a bitter misanthrope who spends much of his time on stage _____ the world and those in it with _____ taunts and caustic jests.
   a. daunting … lucid
   b. rebutting … prim
   c. reprimanding … posthumous
   d. reviling … sardonic

Denotation and Connotation

A word's **denotation** is its literal meaning—the formal meaning of the word provided by a dictionary. A word's denotation conveys a *neutral* tone.

Words also have informal, implied meanings, or **connotations**—associations that readers or listeners make to the word. Connotations can be either *positive* or *negative*.

Consider these synonyms for the neutral word *bold*:

> *intrepid*   *fearless*   *brazen*   *impudent*

Intrepid and *fearless* have positive connotations, while *brazen* and *impudent* have negative connotations.

Look at these examples of words that are similar in denotation but have different connotations.

NEUTRAL	POSITIVE	NEGATIVE
extra	abundant	superfluous
talk	elucidate	prattle
associate	partner	accomplice

Expressing the Connotation

Read each sentence. Select the word in parentheses that expresses the connotation (positive, negative, or neutral) given at the beginning of the sentence.

positive
1. The rising applause was a(n) (**superfluous, auspicious**) sign of the quality of our performance.

neutral
2. The (**lifeless, inanimate**) carousel provided a contrast to the group of horses and riders parading beside it.

negative
3. He discovered many (**undeveloped, latent**) qualities in himself during his time in the Peace Corps.

neutral
4. My cousin has a(n) (**confirmed, incorrigible**) habit of taking my phone without asking.

positive
5. The tennis player's (**intrepid, brazen**) dive for the ball secured her the winning point.

negative
6. Despite its interesting subject matter, the painting seemed (**fated, destined**) to not attract anyone's attention.

positive
7. The mountain climber was (**daunted, emboldened**) by the fog and snow up ahead.

neutral
8. My sister (**absconded with, acquired**) our mother's jewels after the funeral.

Classical Roots

ten, tain, tin—to hold, keep

This root appears in **tenacious** (page 83), which means, literally, "full of holding power." Some other words based on the same root are listed below.

abstention	detention	retinue	tenor
detain	pertain	sustenance	tenure

From the list of words above, choose the one that corresponds to each of the brief definitions below. Write the word in the blank space in the illustrative sentence below the definition. Use an online or print dictionary if necessary.

1. the means of support or subsistence; nourishment

During her ordeal, she drew _____ from her supportive family.

2. the act of doing without; refraining

The doctor advised the patient to observe total _____ from fatty foods to prevent another heart attack.

3. to prevent from going on, delay, hold back; hold as a prisoner

"This traffic jam may _____ us for so long that we will miss our flight," he complained.

4. confinement; holding in custody

The temporary holding cells in that impoverished country were dank and filthy places of _____.

5. to have reference to; to be suitable; to belong, as an attribute or accessory

An attorney can only introduce evidence that directly _____ to the case.

6. a body of followers, group of attendants

The delegation consisted of the king and his loyal _____ of advisors and protectors.

7. the flow of meaning through something written or spoken, drift; the highest adult male voice

He auditioned for the lead _____ role in the opera *Tosca*.

8. the time during which something is held; a permanent right to an office or position after a trial period

The Constitution limits a president's _____ to two consecutive four-year terms of office.

*Read the following passage, taking note of the **boldface** words and their contexts. These words are among those you will be studying in Unit 7. It may help you to complete the exercises in this Unit if you refer to the way the words are used below.*

City Critters
<Humorous Essay>

The **metropolis** is full of life. Millions of people live together in the city, coming and going, day and night. They stream from their homes each morning, off to work and school. The city's an exciting place, full of things to discover: restaurants and shops, playgrounds and parks, theaters and concert halls. But it's a crowded place, and if there's anything millions of people are good at doing when they get together, it's creating **exorbitant** amounts of trash. The trash bags pile up higher each day, while careless citizens litter in the streets, and all this mess attracts unwelcome guests.

Beneath the **obstreperous** traffic of the streets, rats scavenge for food among the waste we leave behind. The **vagrant** rats that wander through our cities can grow to be ten inches long and two pounds in weight. Some urban rats live underground, **meandering** through the sewers and subways, while others nest in alleyways and in proximity to parks or garbage cans. A few creep into our homes through water pipes and holes in walls. Do you think you might like to see a two-pound rat staring at you from the kitchen sink? Think again: A meeting with a **surly** rat can be a **perilous** situation.

Less nasty than the rat is the mighty cockroach. The largest roach you'll find in most American cities is only two inches long. But if you've ever seen one speeding across the floor, or seen a countertop **inundated** with **sprightly** roaches scrambling for cover, you won't forget the sight. No wonder the cockroach is so often **maligned**! Roaches sneak into homes, like rats, through cracks and pipes or through tiny spaces left by **shoddy** repairs. What do you suppose these creepy insects are doing in human dwellings? They're looking for food, just like rats.

The bedbug is even smaller than the cockroach—only ¼-inch in length and difficult to spot. Bedbugs hide in mattresses, in carpeting and furniture, and in cracks and crevices in walls. They creep out while you're asleep,

attracted by your body heat and breath. These little critters aren't looking for the food you've dropped; they aim to feed on you! In the **interim** between the time you go to bed and wake up in the morning, a bedbug will crawl onto your body and feed on your blood, like a mosquito does, for up to five minutes. The next day, you'll find a small, red, irritating bump, the telltale sign of the bedbug bite. Once bedbugs have infested your home, they're difficult to get rid of without the assistance of an exterminator. The best way to prevent infestation is to frequently vacuum dusty areas in your home, including mattresses.

The **advent** of pesticides has limited the spread of vermin, but with so many pests to keep at bay, keeping our homes and cities clean remains a **momentous** task. Don't make **bogus** excuses: Keep kitchens and bathrooms clean and dry, and put food away when you're finished eating. Don't let much time pass between housecleaning days, and refrain from littering in streets and public spaces. We may not ever say **adieu** to all the pests that dwell among us. But we can each do something to keep the places where we live clean and free of pests that thrive in the mess that humans leave behind.

Audio

For ¡Words and audio passages, go to SadlierConnect.com.

Definitions

Note the spelling, pronunciation, part(s) of speech, and definition(s) of each of the following words. Then write the appropriate form of the word in the blank space in the illustrative sentence(s) following.

1. adieu
(ə dü'; a dyü')

(*int.*) "Farewell!"; (*n.*) a farewell
As my friends boarded the airplane, I waved to them and shouted, "_____! Have a safe trip."
I made my _____ to the hosts and left.

2. advent
(ad' vent)

(*n.*) an arrival; a coming into place or view
The _____ of spring is particularly welcome after a long, harsh winter.

3. exorbitant
(eg zôr' bə tənt)

(*adj.*) unreasonably high; excessive
Management rejected the union's demands for higher wages and better benefits as _____.

4. inundate
(in' ən dāt)

(*v.*) to flood, overflow; to overwhelm by numbers or size
Torrential rains and high tides _____ the streets of the picturesque seaside community.

5. malign
(mə līn')

(*v.*) to speak evil of, slander; (*adj.*) evil
In every office, there are gossips who are only too willing to _____ their coworkers.
Iago reveals his _____ motives to the audience in a series of soliloquies.

6. metropolis
(mə träp' ə ləs)

(*n.*) a large city; the chief city of an area
Archaeologists have learned much about the Mayans from the ruins of the _____ Palenque.

7. obstreperous
(əb strep' ər əs)

(*adj.*) noisy; unruly, disorderly
Our teacher will not tolerate _____ behavior in the classroom.

8. perilous
(per' ə ləs)

(*adj.*) dangerous
Episodes of old-time movie serials usually ended with the hero or heroine in _____ circumstances.

9. shoddy
(shäd' ē)

(*adj.*) of poor quality; characterized by inferior workmanship
That designer watch I bought from a street vendor turned out to be a _____ knockoff.

10. vagrant
(vā' grənt)

(*n.*) an idle wanderer, tramp; (*adj.*) wandering aimlessly
During the Great Depression, many people lost everything and were forced to live as _____.
Advertisers continually vie with one another to capture the _____ attention of fickle consumers.

Using Context

*For each item, determine whether the **boldface** word from pages 102–103 makes sense in the context of the sentence. Circle the item numbers next to the six sentences in which the words are used correctly.*

1. My grandparents enjoy telling us about typewriters, answering machines, and other devices that were common before the **advent** of the computer age.

2. The flyer for the grand opening of the new supermarket promises a fantastic selection of items at **exorbitant** prices.

3. If you subscribe to this retailer's mailing list, the company will **inundate** you with catalogs and flyers.

4. No matter how hard I tried to concentrate on my math notes, **vagrant** thoughts of the day's events kept going through my mind.

5. Is there anything as **shoddy** as a cup of hot cocoa on a cold winter day?

6. In the early 1800s, New York City, now a great **metropolis**, received the nickname *Gotham*—which, surprisingly, means "goat town" in old Anglo-Saxon.

7. The opening words of a novel should clearly **malign** the reader and make him or her want to keep reading.

8. When the historic old theater closes its doors forever, we will have to bid it a sad **adieu**.

9. Learning to play a musical instrument is an **obstreperous** process that can take several years.

10. A climber's descent from the summit of Mount Everest can be just as **perilous** as the ascent, perhaps even more so because of fatigue from the climb.

Choosing the Right Word

Select the **boldface** word that better completes each sentence. You might refer to the passage on pages 100–101 to see how most of these words are used in context. Note that the choices might be related forms of the Unit words.

1. I feel that a symphony orchestra is just as important to a (**vagrant, metropolis**) as a big department store or a major-league sports team.

2. I don't know which is worse—your failure to keep your promise or your (**obstreperous, shoddy**) excuse for lying about it.

3. My uncle, an accomplished musician who can play several instruments, is always (**maligned, inundated**) with requests to play at weddings and parties.

4. Churchill once said that if a nation tries to avoid everything that is hard and (**shoddy, perilous**), it will weaken its own security.

5. I lay there quietly, looking at the clouds and allowing (**vagrant, exorbitant**) thoughts to pass through my mind.

6. She admired her supervisor and could not believe that any of her coworkers could possibly have made a (**malign, shoddy**) comment against him.

7. You have reached the stage of life where you must expect to say (**advent, adieu**) to childhood and take on the responsibilities of a young adult.

8. Only after Lincoln's death did most people appreciate the great qualities of the man who had been so (**maligned, inundated**) in his own lifetime.

9. The (**metropolis, advent**) of texting has revolutionized the way in which people communicate with one another.

10. The bylaws state that any member who speaks in a(n) (**obstreperous, perilous**) manner is to be quieted by the sergeant at arms.

11. I know that you're eager to have that pretty dress for the junior prom, but don't you think the price is a little (**perilous, exorbitant**)?

12. When we asked for suggestions on how to improve our school's athletic program, we were (**maligned, inundated**) by "bright ideas" from all sides.

Completing the Sentence

Choose the word from the word bank that best completes each of the following sentences. Write the correct word or form of the word in the space provided.

adieu	exorbitant	malign	obstreperous	shoddy
advent	inundate	metropolis	perilous	vagrant

1. In the streets of all our great cities, you will find _____ who wander about without homes, jobs, or friends.

2. How can you criticize me for the way I behaved during the emergency when you have never been in such a(n) _____ position yourself?

3. When vacant apartments are in short supply, landlords can often get away with charging _____ rents.

4. Shakespeare's wicked characters often assume the guise of kindness to cloak their _____ natures.

5. The food processor certainly looked impressive, but its construction was so _____ that within a few months it began to fall apart.

6. Babysitters often find that children described by their parents as well behaved become _____ brats as soon as those parents leave the house.

7. With the _____ of fast-food restaurants, the appearance of many a main street was forever transformed.

8. The people living in the valley will have to leave their homes because the area will be _____ when a new dam is constructed across the river.

9. "This great _____ has many problems," the mayor said, "but it also has much to offer both residents and visitors."

10. It is sad to have to bid _____ to friends we have known for many years.

Definitions

Note the spelling, pronunciation, part(s) of speech, and definition(s) of each of the following words. Then write the appropriate form of the word in the blank space in the illustrative sentence(s) following.

1. apex
(ā′ peks)

(*n.*) the highest point, tip
    If you want to reach the _____ of the Washington Monument, take the stairs or an elevator.

2. assimilate
(ə sim′ ə lāt)

(*v.*) to absorb fully; to adopt as one's own; to adapt fully
    A well-read person _____ knowledge of a wide range of subjects.

3. bogus
(bō′ gəs)

(*adj.*) false, counterfeit
    Cashiers receive special training so that they will be able to identify _____ currency.

4. interim
(in′ tər əm)

(*n.*) the time between; (*adj.*) temporary, coming between two points in time
    In the _____ between landing and takeoff, the ground crew cleaned and refueled the plane.
    The team played well under an _____ coach for the final three months of the season.

5. meander
(mē an′ dər)

(*v.*) to wander about, wind about; (*n.*) a sharp turn or twist
    When I travel, I like to _____ through unfamiliar towns and cities.
    Lombard Street in San Francisco is famous for its many _____.

6. momentous
(mō men′ təs)

(*adj.*) very important
    A _____ decision by the Supreme Court in 1954 declared public school segregation unconstitutional.

7. pensive
(pen′ siv)

(*adj.*) thoughtful; melancholy
    We admired the skill with which the artist captured the child's _____ expression.

8. sprightly
(sprīt′ lē)

(*adj.*) lively, full of life; spicy, flavorful
    Though Grandmother is well into her eighties, she is still as _____ as a teenager.

9. surly
(sər′ lē)

(*adj.*) angry and bad-tempered; rude

Passengers stranded in an airport because their flight is canceled may become quite _____.

10. tirade
(tī′ rād)

(*n.*) a long, angry speech, usually very critical

The dictator's televised _____ against his opponents lasted for four hours.

Using Context

*For each item, determine whether the **boldface** word from pages 106–107 makes sense in the context of the sentence. Circle the item numbers next to the six sentences in which the words are used correctly.*

1. The protestor refused to end his **tirade** against the company until security was called to escort him out.

2. The con artist was arrested for selling **bogus** paintings as genuine works of famous artists.

3. The **interim** principal will remain in charge until we find a permanent replacement.

4. Let's **meander** to the ticket booth because that tour is known to sell out quickly.

5. With her habitual tardiness and reputation for missing deadlines, the executive quickly rose to the **apex** of the organization.

6. His **surly** greeting indicated that the meeting would be productive and enjoyable.

7. She found the play to be so boring and **momentous** that she left an hour early.

8. I must have had a **pensive** look on my face because my parents asked what was on my mind.

9. Although the dog is almost three years old, her **sprightly** way of walking leads many to believe she is still a puppy.

10. It can take a while for people who move to a new country to fully **assimilate** to the culture and feel part of the community.

Choosing the Right Word

*Select the **boldface** word that better completes each sentence. You might refer to the passage on pages 100–101 to see how most of these words are used in context. Note that the choices might be related forms of the Unit words.*

1. Most people agree that Elizabethan drama reached its (**apex, tirade**) in the matchless plays of Shakespeare.

2. It was amazing to see how that quiet, (**pensive, sprightly**) teenager changed into a tough, hard-driving leader.

3. One of the glories of America has been its ability to (**assimilate, meander**) immigrants from every part of the globe.

4. I suffered a substantial financial loss and an even greater loss of faith in human nature when I tried to cash his (**pensive, bogus**) check.

5. When the new recruits refused to budge from their foxholes, the enraged sergeant let loose with a(n) (**apex, tirade**) of insults and abuse.

6. The governor appointed a member of the state assembly to serve as a(n) (**bogus, interim**) senator until a new election can be held.

7. Her talk (**assimilated, meandered**) aimlessly through memories of her youth, descriptions of her children, and criticisms of the administration.

8. If we have to wait for him to arrive before starting the show, it would be a good idea for us to practice our act in the (**interim, apex**).

9. Was any event in American history more (**momentous, bogus**) than the decision of the Continental Congress in 1776 to break away from Great Britain?

10. My mother's recipe for lemon meringue pie is a (**pensive, sprightly**) blend of tartness and sweetness.

11. The trail that winds through the park (**assimilates, meanders**) through a variety of settings: the Japanese garden, the koi pond, the rose garden, and the pavilion area.

12. I have no respect for people who are unfailingly courteous to their superiors but (**sprightly, surly**) to the employees under them.

Completing the Sentence

Choose the word from the word bank that best completes each of the following sentences. Write the correct word or form of the word in the space provided.

apex	bogus	meander	pensive	surly
assimilate	interim	momentous	sprightly	tirade

1. Many students take jobs during the _____ between the end of one school year and the beginning of the next.

2. When the head of your golf club has reached the _____ of the swing, pause for a second before you begin the downward motion.

3. When the band struck up a(n) _____ tune, even the most reserved party guests began to laugh, dance, and have fun.

4. The notorious jewel thief evaded capture for years by adopting numerous clever disguises and _____ identities.

5. The senator departed from his prepared remarks to deliver an intemperate _____ attacking the administration's foreign policy.

6. The difficult choice between going to college and getting a job is indeed a(n) _____ one for a young person.

7. King's Highway, an old American Indian trail, _____ through Brooklyn, crossing many streets and almost retracing its path at some points.

8. My friend interrupted my _____ mood with the quip "A penny for your thoughts."

9. It takes many long hours of study to _____ all the technical information you need to know if you wish to become a computer programmer.

10. Is there anything more unpleasant than to go to a store and find yourself in the hands of a(n) _____ salesperson?

Synonyms

*Choose the word or form of the word from this Unit that is the same or most nearly the same in meaning as the **boldface** word or expression in the phrase. Write that word on the line. Use a dictionary if necessary.*

1. foreign words **incorporated** into English   _____

2. **roamed** through the beautiful gardens   _____

3. a group of **rowdy** fans   _____

4. anticipated the **arrival** of the mobile phone   _____

5. made of **flimsy** material   _____

6. an **urban center** with many commercial buildings   _____

7. the **crowning point** of a brilliant career   _____

8. the **provisional** head of the department   _____

9. **good-bye**, dear friend   _____

10. a **portentous** meeting of world leaders   _____

11. enjoyed the **animated** conversation   _____

12. music that suits my **wistful** state of mind   _____

13. provides **drifters** with hot meals and shelter   _____

14. **overwhelm** with information   _____

15. refused to respond to my opponent's **harangue**   _____

Antonyms

*Choose the word or form of the word from this Unit that is most nearly opposite in meaning to the **boldface** word or expression in the phrase. Write that word on the line. Use a dictionary if necessary.*

1. in a **friendly** mood   _____

2. paid a **reasonable** price   _____

3. gave her a **genuine** diamond   _____

4. **praise** the coach for her decision   _____

5. a **safe** journey through hostile territory   _____

Writing: Words in Action

In a brief problem-and-solution essay, describe at least one way in which humans can be "pests" themselves in causing harm to the environment, and suggest how this problem can be improved or even solved. Use examples from your reading (pages 100–101) and personal experiences, and three or more words from this Unit.

Vocabulary in Context

*Some of the words you have studied in this Unit appear in **boldface** type. Read the passage below, and then circle the letter of the correct answer for each word as it is used in context.*

What do we mean when we describe our fellow creatures as "intelligent"? What is it that we recognize in, say, chimpanzees, dolphins, elephants, cats, and dogs? Chimps are resourceful; they imitate, communicate with each other, and make tools. Dolphins play, cooperate, and compete in groups. Elephants remember and learn. Cats adapt without losing their independence, and dogs display loyalty and obedience. Of course, it's human qualities that we recognize as signs of intelligence and by doing so we are confirming our own slightly **perilous** position at the **apex** of the intelligent world.

The idea of the intelligence of insects is hard for us to **assimilate**. How can we begin to recognize intelligence in creatures we find generally **malign**, alien, and inscrutable? When we compare people to insects it's invariably insulting. To quote Hamlet when a courtier he dislikes approaches, "Dost know this water-fly?" It's difficult to know just what he means by the insult, for what do we know about insects in terms of personality or character, let alone mind or consciousness? And yet we know that **pensive** Hamlet means it for an insult as sure as if he'd expressed his feeling in a long **tirade**.

It's difficult to know if insects have the capacity for thinking, knowing, remembering, judging, and problem-solving. We can only observe the activities of creatures whose modes of intelligence are unimaginably different from our own. The honeybee, for instance, is born without innate behaviors but develops the ability to identify flowers, gather nectar, count, measure distances greater than a mile, register direction, identify landmarks—and to communicate this information through complex body language. We can't differentiate honeybees, but they can tell us apart and remember our faces. How "intelligent" they are is impossible to tell—but they certainly know things humans cannot understand.

---

1. If you are in a **perilous** position, you are
  a. safe
  b. in danger
  c. lost
  d. at sea

2. The **apex** of something is the
  a. way up
  b. top
  c. middle
  d. heart

3. If an idea is hard to **assimilate** it is almost
  a. acceptable
  b. intractable
  c. unfortunate
  d. incomprehensible

4. Something **malign** is
  a. wretched
  b. ill-spoken
  c. colorful
  d. evil

5. To be **pensive** is to be
  a. thoughtful
  b. kind
  c. sleepy
  d. thoughtless

6. The word **tirade** most nearly means
  a. speech
  b. shout
  c. rant
  d. dissertation

*Read the following passage, taking note of the **boldface** words and their contexts. These words are among those you will be studying in Unit 8. It may help you to complete the exercises in this Unit if you refer to the way the words are used below.*

A History of Sound Recording
<Encyclopedia Entry>

Sound recording is the mechanical or electrical re-creation of sound waves, such as the spoken voice, singing, or instrumental music. Musical clocks and music boxes, some dating to the 1600s, were the first devices to re-create sound. Able to delight a family or **console** a child, these devices had obvious limitations. Most played only one melody, and they could not record a live performance. They also had to be cranked by hand, and the music quickly faded away as the spring mechanism wound down.

Early Sound Recording

Thomas Edison invented the first "talking machine" in 1877. This device recorded sounds on tinfoil wrapped around a cylinder. With every **assurance** of success, the inventor **instituted** the Edison Record Company. Flat disks, invented by Emil Berliner in 1887, improved the quality of the sound, and by 1900, the production of records was an international industry.

Early sound recordings relied on acoustical means to amplify the sound. Huge, **preposterous**-looking horns on early record players were needed to magnify the sound. The invention of vacuum tubes in the early 1920s eliminated this **liability**. Microphones replaced acoustic horns, and the modern electric phonograph was born. The 78 rpm record, made of shellac and later plastic, became the standard.

Sound Recording and Popular Culture

In the **realm** of popular culture, recorded sound had a major impact. In the home, piano-playing and other live music became less common as people listened to records instead. The number of jobs for bands **dwindled**, and many musicians lost their jobs. On the other hand, sound recording **remunerated** popular singers well, and many became rich. When movie makers began recording sound on film in the late 1920s, movies became even more popular.

Early phonographs had huge horns to amplify the sound.

Record players were a popular way to listen to music at home for much of the twentieth century.

Long playing record (above) and tape cassettes (below)

Reel-to-reel tape deck

Digital recording has many modern applications.

Later Developments

As new inventions **rejuvenated** the industry, the **dross** of old equipment was replaced by new technology. In 1948, long-playing records (LPs) appeared, allowing 30 minutes of playing time per side. Ten years later, stereophonic recordings made their debut. With two channels of sound in each groove of the record, stereo produced sound of **sterling** quality.

Recording tape, a thin film coated with magnetic material, had been used to record sound in radio stations since the 1950s. By the mid-1960s, portable tape recorders were available for consumers. Unlike records, tapes did not scratch or **warp**, and people liked the convenience of small tape cassettes, which could be used in cars and portable players. As a result, tape cassettes wound up shouldering out traditional LPs, and the next two decades saw an increasingly **sparse** demand for records.

Digital Recording

Unlike earlier types of sound recording, digital recording converts sound into binary (base-2) numbers. These numbers are then recorded on tape as a series of pulses. Digital compact discs (CDs), read by a laser, came on the market in the early 1980s. Within a decade, CDs were by far the most common way to listen to music, although some music lovers **pugnaciously** defended the sound quality of vinyl records.

The rise of the Internet in the 1990s led to a new **venture** in sound recording. Digital downloads of music to personal listening devices became popular, cutting into CD sales.

While it is often **flippant** to predict the future, the rapid pace of change in sound recording is likely to continue. New ways to listen to music are sure to come.

Related Articles

Acoustics

Digital Technology

Edison, Thomas

Microphone

Phonograph

Audio

For iWords and audio passages, go to SadlierConnect.com.

Definitions

Note the spelling, pronunciation, part(s) of speech, and definition(s) of each of the following words. Then write the appropriate form of the word in the blank space in the illustrative sentence(s) following.

1. asylum
(ə sī′ ləm)

(*n.*) an institution for the care of children, elderly people, etc.; a place of safety

Some refugees are political fugitives who have fled their homeland to seek _____ in another country.

2. console
(*v.*, kən sōl′; *n.*, kän′ sōl)

(*v.*) to comfort; (*n.*) the keyboard of an organ; a control panel for an electrical or mechanical device

A neighbor tried to _____ the sobbing child whose cat had wandered away.

The _____ of the large church organ had an assortment of keys, knobs, and pedals.

3. dwindle
(dwin′ dəl)

(*v.*) to lessen, diminish

During the coldest weeks of winter, the pile of firewood slowly _____ until there were no logs left.

4. flippant
(flip′ ənt)

(*adj.*) lacking in seriousness; disrespectful, saucy

Parents and other adults are often upset by a teenager's _____ responses.

5. liability
(lī ə bil′ ə tē)

(*n.*) a debt; something disadvantageous

A limited attention span is his biggest _____ as a student.

6. pugnacious
(pəg nā′ shəs)

(*adj.*) quarrelsome, fond of fighting

The fox terrier is a particularly _____ breed of dog known for its aggressive behavior.

7. realm
(relm)

(*n.*) a kingdom; a region or field of study

While astronomy falls within the _____ of science, astrology does not.

8. rejuvenate
(ri jü′ və nāt)

(*v.*) to make young again; to make like new

A few minutes of conversation with my best friend helped to _____ my flagging spirits.

9. **sterling** (stər′ liŋ)	(*adj.*) genuine, excellent; made of silver of standard fineness The reviewer noted the young actor's _____ performance in *A Midsummer Night's Dream*.
10. **warp** (wôrp)	(*v.*) to twist out of shape; (*n.*) an abnormality The carpenter explained that humidity caused the kitchen door to _____. Criminal behavior often shows a striking lack of judgment or a _____ in thinking.

Using Context

*For each item, determine whether the **boldface** word from pages 114–115 makes sense in the context of the sentence. Circle the item numbers next to the six sentences in which the words are used correctly.*

1. *Algorithm, data,* and *coding* are all terms from the **realm** of computer science.

2. We tried to find the right words to **console** our cousins after their home was damaged by a hurricane.

3. If you work hard and spend your money wisely, the funds in your bank account are sure to **dwindle**.

4. In *Romeo and Juliet*, Tybalt is a **pugnacious** character whose aggressive behavior has terrible consequences.

5. Because of its **sterling** reputation, that business has had difficulty attracting customers and investors.

6. It is never appropriate to make **flippant** remarks during a serious occasion.

7. Fans pinned their hopes on the promising rookie and expected him to be a huge **liability** for the team.

8. Dry air and direct sunlight can **rejuvenate** an oil painting, causing it to crack and fade.

9. When people feel that they are in danger in their own country because of their beliefs, they might seek political **asylum** in another country.

10. The moist atmosphere of the basement will **warp** the wooden ladder, making it unstable and unsafe to climb.

Choosing the Right Word

Select the **boldface** word that better completes each sentence. You might refer to the passage on pages 112–113 to see how most of these words are used in context. Note that the choices might be related forms of the Unit words.

1. My dog's behavior in obedience class is usually (**pugnacious, sterling**), but yesterday he was more interested in playing with the other dogs than in paying attention to commands.

2. Do you expect me to be (**dwindled, consoled**) by the fact that I was not the only one to fail the exam?

3. Patriotism is a fine quality, but not when it is (**dwindled, warped**) into a hatred of other nations.

4. The outworn ideas of the past cannot be (**rejuvenated, consoled**) simply by expressing them in snappy, modern slang.

5. I support the team captain because of the (**sterling, flippant**) leadership she has given us during the long, hard season.

6. Generally, (**pugnacious, sterling**) behavior on the football field is more effective in drawing penalties than in gaining ground.

7. When you write so imaginatively about "life on other planets," you are entering the (**realm, console**) of science fiction.

8. An unwillingness to listen to suggestions from others is a grave (**liability, realm**) in a leader.

9. How quickly interest in the program (**dwindles, rejuvenates**) when students realize that it calls for so much work, with little chance for glory!

10. Many Americans think that the United States should continue to provide (**liability, asylum**) to people fleeing from tyranny in other lands.

11. When the thief stepped up to the computer (**realm, console**), I knew at once that she had the secret passwords.

12. I like humor as well as anyone, but I don't believe in being (**flippant, sterling**) on so solemn an occasion.

Completing the Sentence

Choose the word from the word bank that best completes each of the following sentences. Write the correct word or form of the word in the space provided.

asylum	dwindle	liability	realm	sterling
console	flippant	pugnacious	rejuvenate	warp

1. I consider myself a very peaceful person, but if anyone approaches me in a(n) _____ manner, I am prepared to defend myself.

2. The wooden staircase we had worked so hard to build was now irregularly curved because the boards had _____.

3. Did you know that the English word *bedlam* was taken from the name of an infamous _____ for the insane in medieval London?

4. She is an excellent ball handler and a very good shot; her only serious _____ as a basketball player is lack of speed.

5. As days passed without a phone call, a letter, or an email, his hopes for even a small role in the production _____.

6. When we are discussing serious social issues, I feel that _____ remarks are in bad taste.

7. Although I cannot support her in the election, I fully appreciate her many _____ qualities.

8. Weary from months of hard work, he was hopeful that a week of camping with friends would _____ him.

9. When my pet hamster died suddenly, even my closest friends were unable to _____ me during my hours of grief.

10. Because her army was stronger than her rival's, the pretender to the throne was able to seize power throughout the entire _____.

Definitions

Note the spelling, pronunciation, part(s) of speech, and definition(s) of each of the following words. Then write the appropriate form of the word in the blank space in the illustrative sentence(s) following.

1. **assurance**
   (ə shu̇r′ əns)

   (*n.*) a pledge; freedom from doubt, self-confidence

   The airport was built with the _____ that all the people displaced by its construction would be fairly compensated.

2. **dilate**
   (dī′ lāt)

   (*v.*) to make or become larger or wider; to expand upon

   The ophthalmologist said she would _____ the pupil before examining the injured eye.

3. **dross**
   (drôs)

   (*n.*) refuse, waste products

   The _____ from the manufacturing process turned out to be highly toxic.

4. **immunity**
   (i myü′ nə tē)

   (*n.*) resistance to disease; freedom from some charge or obligation

   Most babies are vaccinated so that they develop an _____ to measles.

5. **institute**
   (in′ stə tüt)

   (*v.*) to establish, set up; (*n.*) organization that promotes learning

   Congress has been reluctant to _____ new guidelines for campaign spending.

   After graduating from high school, I plan to attend an accredited _____ of technology.

6. **preposterous**
   (prē päs′ tər əs)

   (*adj.*) ridiculous, senseless

   The theory that Stonehenge was constructed by alien life-forms is utterly _____.

7. **rabid**
   (rab′ id)

   (*adj.*) furious, violently intense, unreasonably extreme; mad; infected with rabies

   Police arrived in force to quell the riot set off by _____ soccer fans.

8. **remunerate**
   (ri myü′ nə rāt)

   (*v.*) to reward, pay, reimburse

   The couple promised to _____ the artist handsomely for a portrait of their child.

9. **sparse**
(spärs)

(*adj.*) meager, scant; scattered
Unlike its neighboring metropolis, the area has quite a _____ population.

10. **venture**
(ven' chər)

(*n.*) a risky or daring undertaking; (*v.*) to expose to danger; to dare
An overseas voyage was a daunting and dangerous _____ during the Age of Exploration.
It takes courage to _____ out into unknown territory.

Using Context

*For each item, determine whether the **boldface** word from pages 118–119 makes sense in the context of the sentence. Circle the item numbers next to the six sentences in which the words are used correctly.*

1. When the troops find out that they are vastly outnumbered, they will **venture** to the safety of their base camp.

2. Dedicated fans of the television show were **rabid** when the main character was written out in the middle of the season.

3. We underestimated the amount of food we would need on the camping trip, so our supply was **sparse** after only two days.

4. The guest speaker's engaging presentation was full of **dross** and inspiring anecdotes.

5. Getting enough sleep is important to staying healthy and helping your body develop **immunity** to illnesses.

6. The founding fathers decided to **institute** a system of checks and balances by dividing power among the three branches of the U.S. government.

7. She was determined to **remunerate** the unnecessary fees that the contractor had charged her.

8. The landlord asked me to provide **assurance** that I could afford the rent by supplying proof of income.

9. The movie's **preposterous** ending felt jarring compared to its down-to-earth beginning.

10. I had to **dilate** my essay before turning it in, as I had exceeded the maximum page length.

Choosing the Right Word

Select the **boldface** word that better completes each sentence. You might refer to the passage on pages 112–113 to see how most of these words are used in context. Note that the choices might be related forms of the Unit words.

1. Today scientists smile wryly at the (**preposterous, sparse**) notion that the earth is flat, but in earlier times it was an accepted fact.

2. I would not agree to run for public office before receiving (**assurance, dross**) of support from important groups in the community.

3. I agree with some of the speaker's ideas, but I find her (**rabid, sparse**) enthusiasm for crackpot causes hard to take.

4. The college swim team went on an overseas (**dross, venture**) to compete with teams from all parts of Southeast Asia.

5. The hired man agreed to testify against his boss in exchange for (**immunity, assurance**) against charges related to the crime.

6. The (**institute, venture**) had a strict policy that new members could not be admitted without a thorough review and background check.

7. To meet stricter industry standards, manufacturers will have to (**institute, remunerate**) new systems of quality control.

8. No doubt the instructor knows a great deal about ecology, but is there any need for her to (**venture, dilate**) on threats to the environment at such great length?

9. As usual, there are plenty of *talkers*, but the supply of *doers* is (**rabid, sparse**).

10. I know better than to (**dilate, venture**) into a canoe that a novice will paddle upstream against a crosswind.

11. In spite of all his talk about his great wealth, I noticed that the penny-pincher did not offer to (**institute, remunerate**) us for expenses.

12. Clear away the (**immunity, dross**) of false ideas from your mind and take a long, hard look at reality.

Completing the Sentence

Choose the word from the word bank that best completes each of the following sentences. Write the correct word or form of the word in the space provided.

assurance	dross	institute	rabid	sparse
dilate	immunity	preposterous	remunerate	venture

1. As the snake came into view and slithered across her path, the archaeologist's eyes _____ with fear.

2. He is such a(n) _____ sports enthusiast that he spends almost all of his spare time either playing ball or watching ball games on television.

3. The philanthropist devoted her time, energy, and funds to establishing a(n) _____ for promoting world peace.

4. The idea that an incoming president can miraculously solve all of the nation's problems is simply _____.

5. Calling upon his many years of experience, the retired warden discussed with great _____ the topic of the evening: "Can Criminals Be Rehabilitated?"

6. You will need experience, ability, financing, and good luck to have any chance of succeeding in so risky a business _____.

7. Can any amount of money _____ someone for years sacrificed to a hopeless cause?

8. Doctors hope to lessen the number, length, and severity of common colds, even if they cannot provide complete _____ from them.

9. Despite intense heat, meager rainfall, and _____ vegetation, many animals have adapted to life in the desert.

10. The main point of my sister's speech was that all the riches of the world are so much worthless _____ without the support of one's friends.

Synonyms

*Choose the word or form of the word from this Unit that is the same or most nearly the same in meaning as the **boldface** word or expression in the phrase. Write that word on the line. Use a dictionary if necessary.*

1. the **fanatical** ravings of a rabble-rouser   _____
2. **compensate** the babysitter for his time   _____
3. seek **refuge** from incessant strife   _____
4. a **sassy** response   _____
5. the **rubbish** from the metal plant   _____
6. **distort** due to humidity   _____
7. an **argumentative** person ready to take offense   _____
8. a potion to **revitalize** and energize   _____
9. **soothe** the family in their sorrow   _____
10. **initiate** a new policy   _____
11. without any **drawback**   _____
12. with **impunity** from prosecution   _____
13. a bold **gamble**   _____
14. cause blood vessels to **swell**   _____
15. the ruler of this **domain**   _____

Antonyms

*Choose the word or form of the word from this Unit that is most nearly opposite in meaning to the **boldface** word or expression in the phrase. Write that word on the line. Use a dictionary if necessary.*

1. an **abundant** food supply   _____
2. a **sensible** idea   _____
3. had **shoddy** qualities   _____
4. gave repeated **denials**   _____
5. begin to **increase** in size   _____

Writing: Words in Action

Write a brief cause-and-effect essay in which you explore the effects of one specific technological advancement in sound recording from the era of your choice. Identify at least one positive and one negative effect. Use at least two details from the passage (pages 112–113) and three or more words from this Unit.

Vocabulary in Context

*Some of the words you have studied in this Unit appear in **boldface** type. Read the passage below, and then circle the letter of the correct answer for each word as it is used in context.*

The introduction of the 12-inch vinyl long-playing record (LP) marked a significant improvement in the sound quality of recorded music. Vinyl was amenable to the new microgroove technology and produced a much cleaner sound than hitherto. LPs were larger and more delicate than 10-inch shellac, so they were marketed from the start in 12-inch square protective covers made out of stiff card. These simple squares would become the medium for one of the most diverse, dynamic, and popular art forms of the twentieth century.

When they first appeared, LP covers displayed the title of the album, the name of the recording artist (or artists), and a list of the individual tracks, but other information was **sparse**. During the fifties jazz album sleeves began to feature abstract designs, and pop stars started to adorn the covers of their records to attract the attention of record-buyers. But it was in the sixties and seventies that the art form came into its own. Looking at an album cover in the distorted and colorful style of the time was enough to **dilate** the mesmerized viewer's pupils.

One of the iconic covers of the period was The Beatles' *Abbey Road* (1969). The album is named for the recording studio that had become an **asylum**, a peaceful **realm** where the fabulously popular group had **immunity** from **rabid** fans. The cover shows the four band members on the crosswalk in front of the studio on a late summer morning. It is one of the last photographs of the band all together, and it emphasizes the separateness and individuality of the band members rather than their group identity. By the time the record was released, The Beatles had split up.

---

1. If information is **sparse**, it is
   a. plentiful
   b. terse
   c. missing
   d. meager

2. If pupils are **dilated**, they are
   a. narrowed
   b. dazzled
   c. tired
   d. expanded

3. An **asylum** is a
   a. place of safety
   b. palace
   c. children's home
   d. bell-tower

4. If you were a monarch, your **realm** would be your
   a. palace
   b. throne
   c. kingdom
   d. subjects

5. The word **immunity** most nearly means
   a. invulnerability
   b. insolubility
   c. freedom from duty
   d. lack of protection

6. A person who is said to be **rabid** is usually
   a. indifferent
   b. obnoxious
   c. driven by a mob
   d. violently intense

*Read the following passage, taking note of the **boldface** words and their contexts. These words are among those you will be studying in Unit 9. It may help you to complete the exercises in this Unit if you refer to the way the words are used below.*

Ringl and Pit: Witnesses to the Weimar
<Profile>

There is an old adage that says, "Success is not measured by what you accomplish but by the opposition you have encountered." Two women who knew the meaning of that type of success generations ago were the pioneering photographers Ellen Rosenberg Auerbach and Grete Stern, better known as Ringl + Pit.

Auerbach and Stern were born in Germany in the early 1900s to middle-class Jewish families. They met in Berlin at the studio of a photography professor at the Bauhaus, the world-famous art and design school, and became fast friends. These creative women discovered that they had a **flair** for photography. They were also ambitious: As so-called new women, they refused to settle for **auxiliary** roles in the workplace. They had no intention of **feigning** interest in the more traditional careers open to women at the time. They wanted the same freedom and choices their male colleagues took for granted. So when their friend from the Bauhaus decided to close his private studio, the young women took over the premises and renamed the business Foto Ringl + Pit. (*Ringl* and *Pit* were the childhood nicknames, respectively, of Stern and Auerbach.)

It was a great time to set up shop because the advertising industry was booming, despite the fragile economic and political state of the Weimar Republic (the period of German history from 1919 to 1933, between the two world wars). Their career move proved to be **expedient**, and Foto Ringl + Pit was a commercial and artistic success. The women discovered they could earn a living using their artistic talents in advertising, publicity, and fashion photography. Their striking photographs were praised for their unique,

Ellen Rosenberg Auerbach and Grete Stern, shown here in 1995, named their groundbreaking photography business after their childhood nicknames, Ringl and Pit.

playful style. While some of their shots were **candid**, most were staged and posed. They also turned their cameras on many celebrated writers, artists, and performers of the day.

But the **prognosis** for peace and longed-for prosperity in Germany was not promising. The country's Jews were already experiencing **grievous** hardships. The **repugnant** beliefs of Hitler and the Nazis soon replaced the tolerant views of the Weimar era. **Hordes** of Jews and other "undesirables" were rounded up and taken to concentration camps; most didn't survive the **drudgery**, illness, starvation, or gas chambers there.

Anti-Semitism **escalated** once Hitler came to power, forcing Ringl + Pit to **scuttle** their plans and working partnership. They were **impelled** to leave Germany. As Ellen Auerbach said years later in a documentary about Ringl + Pit, "In a country with concentration camps, you cannot live." The women eventually settled in Buenos Aires and in New York, places with more open, **heterogeneous** populations than Germany. They continued to work in photography and had impressive solo careers.

Ellen Rosenberg Auerbach and Grete Stern both lived long, extraordinary lives. Although the talented duo of Ringl + Pit never worked together again after the mid-1930s, they stayed lifelong friends. These days, you can see their groundbreaking photographs on display in galleries and museums around the world, and their original prints are highly sought-after (a photo **inscribed** with "Ringl + Pit" can be worth thousands).

Komol, 1931 @ringl+pit/The Metropolitan Museum of Art, courtesy of Robert Mann Gallery, New York, NY

Audio

For iWords and audio passages, go to SadlierConnect.com.

Hat and Gloves, 1932

Pit with Veil, 1930

Definitions

Note the spelling, pronunciation, part(s) of speech, and definition(s) of each of the following words. Then write the appropriate form of the word in the blank space in the illustrative sentence(s) following.

1. cubicle
(kyü′ bə kəl)

(*n.*) a small room or compartment
The tiniest _____ is usually assigned to the newest employee.

2. drudgery
(drəj′ ə rē)

(*n.*) work that is hard and tiresome
Trade unions lobby to relieve the endless _____ of factory workers.

3. escalate
(es′ kə lāt)

(*v.*) to elevate; to increase in intensity
A small dispute can _____ into a major conflict unless the opposing parties sit down and talk.

4. expedient
(ek spē′ dē ənt)

(*n.*) a means to an end; (*adj.*) advantageous, useful
As an _____, we chose to use a rock as a makeshift hammer.
An opportunist is someone who is always ready to do whatever is most _____.

5. grievous
(grē′ vəs)

(*adj.*) causing sorrow or pain; serious
Reporters should take careful notes when interviewing to avoid making _____ errors in print.

6. horde
(hôrd)

(*n.*) a vast number (as of people); a throng
When the doors opened, a _____ of shoppers headed toward the sales racks.

7. impel
(im pel′)

(*v.*) to force, drive forward
Hunger often _____ people to leave their homes in search of food.

8. incredulous
(in krej′ ə ləs)

(*adj.*) disbelieving, skeptical
When the testimony of a witness contradicts the evidence, you can expect _____ stares from the jury.

9. prognosis
(präg nō′ səs)

(*n.*) a forecast of the probable course and outcome of a disease or situation

Doctors are particularly happy to deliver a

_____ of a speedy recovery.

10. repugnant
(rē pəg′ nənt)

(*adj.*) offensive, disagreeable, distasteful

Despite their _____ lack of cleanliness, pigs are endearing to many people.

Using Context

*For each item, determine whether the **boldface** word from pages 126–127 makes sense in the context of the sentence. Circle the item numbers next to the six sentences in which the words are used correctly.*

1. When she was promoted to assistant manager, my sister moved from a **cubicle** to an office.

2. The low hum from the car's engine will **escalate** into a loud rumble as the car picks up speed.

3. The scent of roasting garlic from the kitchen was so **repugnant** that it made us hungry.

4. We agreed that a face-to-face meeting would be more **expedient** than a drawn-out exchange of emails and set the time for 2:00 p.m.

5. Had he not been wearing a seatbelt, he would almost certainly have suffered a **grievous** injury as a result of the car accident.

6. Attempting to bribe a public official is not only **incredulous**, but it is also against the law.

7. While some people find vacuuming a form of **drudgery**, I try to enjoy it as a form of exercise.

8. You need only a **horde** of coins to buy that apple.

9. The landscaper said that there were too many fallen leaves to **impel** the lawn any further.

10. The **prognosis** for patients with certain kinds of cancer is now much better than it was just twenty years ago.

Choosing the Right Word

*Select the **boldface** word that better completes each sentence. You might refer to the passage on pages 124–125 to see how most of these words are used in context. Note that the choices might be related forms of the Unit words.*

1. I don't consider it (**drudgery, expedient**) to prepare meals every day because I love good food and good cooking.

2. I work in an office compartment, travel in a midget car, and sleep in a tiny bedroom. My life seems to take place in a series of (**hordes, cubicles**)!

3. Was it patriotism, a desire to show off, or just self-interest that (**escalated, impelled**) the foreign minister to take those terrible risks?

4. The expression of satisfaction that comes over her face when she talks of the failures of other people is highly (**expedient, repugnant**) to me.

5. An army without strong leadership and firm discipline is no more than an armed (**horde, drudgery**).

6. It was wrong of me to be so curt with him, but it was the (**expedient, incredulous**) thing to do, since I was already running late to my appointment.

7. After examining the price tag, I gingerly replaced the coat on the rack, (**incredulous, grievous**) at the preposterous sum the store was asking for it.

8. Despite the doctor's gloomy (**prognosis, drudgery**) when I entered the hospital, I was up and about in a matter of days.

9. "The noble Brutus has told you Caesar was ambitious; if it were so, it was a(n) (**grievous, incredulous**) fault."

10. Political analysts, students of statecraft, and historians tried to determine what caused a minor border incident to (**escalate, impel**) into a full-scale war.

11. Cut off from all supplies, the soldiers had to use various (**expedients, cubicles**) to keep their equipment in working order.

12. When the cat encountered the dog in the hallway, it assailed the dog with a(n) (**expedient, grievous**) onslaught of scratches and bites.

Completing the Sentence

Choose the word from the word bank that best completes each of the following sentences. Write the correct word or form of the word in the space provided.

cubicle	escalate	grievous	impel	prognosis
drudgery	expedient	horde	incredulous	repugnant

1. An unwilling pupil is apt to look upon hours of practice at the piano as so much boredom and _____.

2. We must have the courage and the clear-sightedness to realize that what is _____ is not always right.

3. My rather lame excuse for failing to complete my homework was greeted with a(n) _____ snort by the teacher.

4. The New York City Marathon begins with a(n) _____ of runners swarming across the Verrazano-Narrows Bridge.

5. When Lincoln had been in the White House for about a year, he suffered a(n) _____ loss in the death of his son Willie.

6. In times of rapid inflation, prices of goods _____ at a dizzying rate.

7. While some people relish Limburger cheese, others find its strong odor truly _____.

8. I maintain that my _____ in the dormitory is so small that I have to walk into the hallway to change my mind or stretch my imagination.

9. I hope you will listen attentively to your parents' dire _____ of the probable effect that a third bowl of chili will have on your digestion.

10. A strong sense of fair play should _____ you to admit your mistake.

Definitions

Note the spelling, pronunciation, part(s) of speech, and definition(s) of each of the following words. Then write the appropriate form of the word in the blank space in the illustrative sentence(s) following.

1. auxiliary
(ôg zil′ yə rē)

(*adj.*) giving assistance or support; (*n.*) a helper, aid
If the main motor fails, the instructions say to turn on the _____ motor.
Someone second in command is an _____ to the person in charge.

2. candid
(kan′ did)

(*adj.*) frank, sincere; impartial; unposed
It is safe to be _____ about our faults with friends and loved ones.

3. envoy
(en′ voi; än′ voi)

(*n.*) a representative or messenger (as of a government)
On more than one occasion, a former President has been asked to act as a special _____ to the United Nations.

4. feign
(fān)

(*v.*) to pretend
Children sometimes _____ illness to avoid going to school.

5. flair
(flâr)

(*n.*) a natural quality, talent, or skill; a distinctive style
An opera singer needs a _____ for the dramatic as well as a good voice.

6. heterogeneous
(het ə rə jē′ nē əs)

(*adj.*) composed of different kinds, diverse
Most college admissions officers actively seek a student body that is both talented and _____.

7. inscribe
(in skrīb′)

(*v.*) to write or engrave; to enter a name on a list
The young man asked the jeweler to _____ the locket with his fiancée's name.

8. monologue
(män′ ə läg)

(*n.*) a speech by one actor; a long talk by one person
By means of a _____, a playwright shares a character's private thoughts with the audience.

9. rasping
(ras′ piŋ)

(*adj.*) with a harsh, grating sound; (*n.*) a harsh sound

Chronic bronchitis can lead to a _____ cough that is difficult to cure.

The _____ of metal scraping against metal sets my teeth on edge.

10. scuttle
(skət′ əl)

(*v.*) to sink a ship by cutting holes in it; to get rid of something in a decisive way; to run hastily, scurry; (*n.*) a pail

Pirates would not wish to _____ a captured galleon before looting its cargo.

Years ago, it was possible to buy a _____ of coal at the corner grocery store.

Using Context

*For each item, determine whether the **boldface** word from pages 130–131 makes sense in the context of the sentence. Circle the item numbers next to the six sentences in which the words are used correctly.*

1. Most hospitals have **auxiliary** power generators that will take over if the electricity goes out.

2. The **scuttle** left on the lawn after the concert took days for the crew to clean up.

3. I was nervous about giving the **monologue**, for if I forgot a line, there would be no one else on stage to prompt me.

4. I asked the jeweler to **inscribe** the bracelet with the words of my favorite quotation.

5. My teacher's **candid** feedback on my essay was hard to take at first, but it eventually helped me to improve my writing.

6. His **flair** for speaking hinders his ability to make impressionable presentations for his team.

7. All members of our book club have a **heterogeneous** taste in literature, so it will be easy to choose novels that everyone will like.

8. I know next to nothing about sports, so I usually have to **feign** interest when someone strikes up a conversation about a recent game.

9. It's been months since I recovered from pneumonia, but I sometimes still have a **rasping** voice if I don't clear my throat before speaking.

10. My friends traveling abroad sent an **envoy** with descriptions about all the sites they have visited.

Choosing the Right Word

*Select the **boldface** word that better completes each sentence. You might refer to the passage on pages 124–125 to see how most of these words are used in context. Note that the choices might be related forms of the Unit words.*

1. I must admit now that I was hurt when the coach took me out in the last minutes of the game, but I tried to (**scuttle, feign**) indifference.

2. I searched in vain through the (**auxiliary, heterogeneous**) pile of odds and ends for the spare part I had inadvertently thrown away.

3. The poet Browning tells us that if we were to open his heart, we would find the word "Italy" (**inscribed, feigned**) inside it.

4. As soon as I heard (**heterogeneous, rasping**) noises coming from the workshop, I knew that someone was using a saw or a file.

5. How can you say that the broadcast interview was spontaneous and (**heterogeneous, candid**) when it was all carefully rehearsed?

6. Instead of sending your little sister as a(n) (**envoy, flair**) to explain what went wrong, why don't you stand up and speak for yourself?

7. When I jolted awake last night to the sound of a desperate (**monologue, rasping**), I was cold with fear until I realized that it was my old dog, who sometimes has breathing problems.

8. People who boast of their high moral principles are often the ones who will (**scuttle, inscribe**) them most quickly to serve their own interests.

9. She handed me a (**scuttle, flair**) of slop for the pigs, and suddenly I was glad that this was a job I did not have to do very often.

10. Since the person I was trying to interview wouldn't let me get a word in edgewise, our conversation quickly turned into a(n) (**envoy, monologue**).

11. It's one thing to be interested in writing; it's quite another to have a (**flair, monologue**) for it.

12. The building is equipped with a(n) (**rasping, auxiliary**) generator, ready to go into service whenever the main power source is cut off.

Completing the Sentence

Choose the word from the word bank that best completes each of the following sentences. Write the correct word or form of the word in the space provided.

| auxiliary | envoy | flair | inscribe | rasping |
| candid | feign | heterogeneous | monologue | scuttle |

1. The names of all four members of the record-breaking relay team are _____ on the trophy awarded to our school.

2. Her voice is so _____ that I find it painful to listen to her speak.

3. A(n) _____ for color and texture is an indispensable asset to an aspiring dress designer.

4. In many cities, groups of private citizens have volunteered to serve as _____ police to help combat crime.

5. Hopelessly cut off from the main fleet, the captain of the vessel decided to _____ his ship rather than allow it to fall into enemy hands.

6. A special _____ was named by the President to negotiate a settlement in the war-torn region.

7. In her opening _____, the talk-show host often pokes fun at political candidates and elected officials.

8. It is all very well to be _____, but there are times when you should keep certain thoughts and opinions to yourself.

9. It is a(n) _____ population that accounts for the wide variety of cultures found in some neighborhoods.

10. I can't help but admire your ability to _____ interest when someone prattles on endlessly about nothing.

Synonyms

*Choose the word or form of the word from this Unit that is the same or most nearly the same in meaning as the **boldface** word or expression in the phrase. Write that word on the line. Use a dictionary if necessary.*

1. **spurred** the residents to take action _____

2. continue to **climb** rapidly _____

3. an optimistic **prediction** for economic recovery _____

4. a **diverse** group of participants _____

5. the **scratchy** tone of an old vinyl record _____

6. the **toil** of endless work _____

7. an endless **recitation** of petty complaints _____

8. an extraordinary **aptitude** for numbers _____

9. **fake** interest in the show _____

10. an **agent** of a foreign government _____

11. suffered a **heartrending** loss _____

12. remained **dubious** of stories about aliens _____

13. rely on the **back-up** speakers _____

14. the small, dark **enclosure** _____

15. the names **imprinted** on a monument _____

Antonyms

*Choose the word or form of the word from this Unit that is most nearly opposite in meaning to the **boldface** word or expression in the phrase. Write that word on the line. Use a dictionary if necessary.*

1. **preserve** the old ship _____

2. told in a **guarded** manner _____

3. the **pleasant** smell _____

4. prepared for the **handful** of customers _____

5. an **ill-advised** action that altered the course of history _____

Writing: Words in Action

Write a brief speech in which you summarize the story of Ringl and Pit, using it as an inspiring anecdote to show your audience that they too can overcome difficult circumstances. Use at least two details from the passage (pages 124–125) and three or more words from this Unit to support your points.

Vocabulary in Context

*Some of the words you have studied in this Unit appear in **boldface** type. Read the passage below, and then circle the letter of the correct answer for each word as it is used in context.*

In late June 1919, **envoys** from Germany arrived in Paris to sign the Treaty of Versailles, which officially ended World War I. Thus was born the Weimar Republic, which governed Germany until 1933. Almost from its beginning, this government was shaken by a series of blows. The peace treaty imposed staggering war reparations, and hyperinflation soon gripped Germany. The price of a cup of coffee could rise 50 percent within an hour. By November 1923, one American dollar was worth 4.3 trillion German marks. Currency was inflating so rapidly that printers of paper money could not keep up. From petty bureaucrats in their **cubicles** to industrial magnates in their mansions, i**ncredulous** Germans fell prey to economic despair.

Curiously, however, this same period in German history witnessed a remarkable cultural renaissance. This flowering in the arts was spearheaded by the design movement known as the Bauhaus, centered in Weimar until 1925 and focused on the style and themes of Modernism. Founded and directed by the pioneering architect Walter Gropius, the Bauhaus soon attained worldwide influence, with brilliant achievements by Paul Klee in painting, Alban Berg and Kurt Weill in music, Fritz Lang in film, and Ludwig Mies van der Rohe in architecture. A **candid** assessment of these artists' achievements would have to concede that the streamlined Bauhaus style is still very much with us. Just look around at the steel and glass skyscrapers of any city today.

The collapse of the Weimar Republic was not long in coming. Adolf Hitler's **rasping** harangues of hatred and fear attracted enormous crowds. His rambling **monologues** promised release from instability and humiliation. Nazi party membership grew by more than 800 percent between 1919 and 1932. The following year, Hitler took power as chancellor of Germany.

---

1. Envoys are
  a. ambassadors   **c.** governors
  b. subordinates   **d.** trustees

2. Working in **cubicles** might easily make people feel
  a. relaxed   **c.** apprehensive
  b. listless   **d.** cramped

3. If you are **incredulous**, you do not
  a. agree   **c.** believe
  b. acknowledge   **d.** object

4. A **candid** person is
  a. skeptical   **c.** casual
  b. forthright   **d.** thorough

5. The word **rasping** most nearly means
  a. garbled   **c.** harsh-sounding
  b. plaintive   **d.** apologetic

6. Which word best describes **monologues**?
  a. lengthy   **c.** practical
  b. courageous   **d.** concise

Vocabulary for Comprehension
Part 1

*Read this passage, which contains words in **boldface** that appear in Units 7–9. Then choose the best answer to each question based on what is stated or implied in the passage. You may refer to the passage as often as necessary.*

Questions 1–10 are based on the following passage.

This passage is adapted from Henry A. Shute, *Plupy*, "*The Real Boy*." Published in 1911.

Left alone, Plupy cut a stout but limber switch and carefully whittled the end to a point on which to impale the apples. If he could only harden the end in fire it would
(5) not split. There was Mr. Dyer's blacksmith shop just across the garden, but Plupy wasn't allowed to go out of the yard because of what he did last evening. Maybe Mr. Dyer would harden the point.
(10) So he climbed the boundary fence and **meandered** over to the blacksmith.
"Mr. Dyer," he called, "will you please harden the end of this stick in your fire?"
Mr. Dyer looked up with a momentary
(15) frown. His experience with Plupy had been somewhat extensive and of such a nature as to put him in a condition of being constantly on guard with the **obstreperous** lad. But Mr. Dyer was
(20) extremely good natured and his frown was speedily chased away by a cheerful grin.
"Of course, come right over," he said.
"I can't—I got to stay in the yard all day," said Plupy, shame-facedly.
(25) "What you been doing now?" said Sam.
"I didn't split the kindlings last night." Plupy did not wish to appear **flippant**. He wanted to be **candid**.
"Hmm, that's a pretty **momentous**
(30) crime," said Sam, "but give me your stick and I'll singe it for you." And he obligingly did so, returning it with the point in a delightfully adamantine condition.
Plupy thanked him and ran back to
(35) fill his pockets with hard green apples. Then, choosing one from the **horde**, he

ventured to bite it and made a wry face, for it was sour and bitter. Then, impaling it on the point, he lightly swung the switch
(40) into the air, then gave it a throwing motion with all the strength of his arm.
"Whoof," sang the switch as it cut through the air, and away went the apple with an audible hum, leaving the point at
(45) just the right moment. Away, away it soared, ascending for an incredible distance before it passed out of sight.
Another was tried with equal success. Plupy forgot all his troubles and was
(50) happy. But to make his happiness complete, some target was necessary.
So Plupy looked about for a target. Across two gardens sat two men on a fence. They had been hired to work in a
(55) neighbor's garden, and in the absence of that neighbor, were making much better use of their time with some political discussion. Their thoughtful stillness made them an irresistible target—not to hit them,
(60) but to cause a kerfuffle nearby.
Plupy's first few shots went like lightning, but landed wide of the mark. Gradually he began to get the range and finally, to his intense delight, a hard round
(65) apple hit a tree trunk in the close vicinity of the disputants with a prodigious smack. In an instant they sprang from the fence with an unforeseen agility and, issuing **pugnacious** promises of retribution,
(70) charged in the direction from which the missile had come.
Plupy ducked and scurried into the barn. He found a hiding place close to a small window, through which he could
(75) follow their endeavors to discover the whereabouts of the miscreant responsible

for launching this airborne offense to common civility and orderliness.

The fervor with which they set about (80) their quest seemed utterly **preposterous** to Plupy. Soon enough, when their search yielded a pair of comfortable chairs, they sat down and continued their discussion of the world and how to improve it.

1. As it is used in line 28, "candid" most nearly means
A) friendly.
B) convincing.
C) frank.
D) serious.

2. As it is used in line 29, "momentous" most nearly means
A) insignificant.
B) temporary.
C) daring.
D) consequential.

3. In lines 29–30, Sam's comment on Plupy's offense is
A) harsh.
B) fair.
C) ironic.
D) judgmental.

4. It can reasonably be inferred from the ninth paragraph (lines 29–33) that Mr. Dyer
A) is fond of Plupy.
B) misjudges Plupy.
C) does not like Plupy.
D) does not know Plupy.

5. The author makes the point in the tenth paragraph (lines 34–41) that Plupy
A) fills his pockets with apples to eat later.
B) collects apples to serve as missiles.
C) only picks apples not worth eating.
D) cannot find any apples worth eating.

6. In lines 54–58, the author indicates that the two men are
A) intellectuals.
B) politicians.
C) philanthropists.
D) shirkers.

7. As it is used in line 69, "pugnacious" most nearly means
A) combative.
B) audacious.
C) laughable.
D) false.

8. It can reasonably be inferred that, as Plupy watches the men from the barn window,
A) he thinks they cannot be looking for him.
B) he thinks they are making a lot more fuss than the offense merits.
C) he is sure they are going to discover where he is hiding.
D) he wonders why they require chairs.

9. Which choice provides the best evidence for the answer to the previous question?
A) Lines 67–71 ("In an . . . had come")
B) Lines 73–78 ("He . . . orderliness")
C) Line 79–81 ("The fervor . . . Plupy")
D) Lines 81–84 ("Soon . . . improve it")

10. Which choice best summarizes the passage?
A) A grounded kid relieves his boredom by using a switch to launch apples in the direction of two strangers.
B) A boy uses a long stick to shoot apples into a neighboring yard, incurring the wrath of two gardeners.
C) A guileful lad tricks a blacksmith into lobbing apples into a neighbor's yard.
D) Two shirking gardeners get a surprise when a kid bombards them with apples.

Vocabulary for Comprehension
Part 2

*Read this passage, which contains words in **boldface** that appear in Units 7–9. Then choose the best answer to each question based on what is stated or implied in the passage. You may refer to the passage as often as necessary.*

Questions 1–10 are based on the following passage.

This passage is adapted from Sir Arthur Conan Doyle, *The Lost World*. Published in 1912.

It was at this point that the sensation of the evening arose—a sensation so dramatic that it can never have been paralleled in the history of scientific
(5) gatherings. Professor Challenger raised his hand in the air as a signal for Malone. An instant later he reappeared in the company of a gigantic porter, the two of them bearing between them a large
(10) square packing case. It was evidently of great weight, and the words "Dangerous Cargo" were **inscribed** on every side.

There was a hush. Professor Challenger drew off the top of the case and snapped
(15) his fingers, and was heard from the Press seats to say, "Come, then, pretty, pretty!"

An instant later, a most horrible and loathsome creature appeared from inside and perched itself upon the side of the
(20) case. Nothing could distract the petrified attention of the vast audience. The face of the creature was like the wildest gargoyle that the **warped** imagination of a mad medieval builder could have conceived. It
(25) was **malign**, horrible, with two small red eyes as bright as points of burning coal. Its long, savage beak, which it held half-open, was full of a double row of shark-like teeth. Its shoulders were
(30) humped, and round them were draped what appeared to be a faded gray shawl.

There was turmoil in the audience— someone screamed, and for a moment matters were truly **perilous**. Professor
(35) Challenger threw up his hands to still the commotion, but the movement alarmed

the creature beside him. Its strange shawl suddenly unfurled, spread wide, and fluttered as if it were preparing to abandon
(40) its precarious perch. Sensing its intent, Professor Challenger made a grab for its legs, but he was too late to hold it. It had sprung from the perch and taken flight, and now was circling slowly round the
(45) Queens Hall with a dry, leathery flapping of its ten-foot wings. A putrid and insidious odor pervaded the room. The cries of people in the galleries, who were alarmed at the near approach of those **rabid**,
(50) glowing eyes and that murderous beak, **impelled** the creature to a frenzy. Faster and faster it flew, beating against walls and chandeliers in **escalating** panic.

"The window! For heaven's sake shut
(55) that window!" roared the Professor from the stage, wringing his hands in an agony of apprehension. Alas, his warning was too late! The creature, bumping along the wall like a huge moth within the shade of
(60) a gas lamp, came upon the opening, squeezed its hideous bulk through it, and was gone out into the **metropolis**.

Nothing can be said for certain as to the fate of the London pterodactyl. Reports
(65) are **sparse**. There was some talk that it perched upon the roof of Queens Hall and remained there like a diabolical statue for some hours. The only reliable evidence I have been able to find comes from the
(70) log of the *SS. Friesland*, a Dutch-American liner, where it is reported that soon after nine o'clock on the morning after the pterodactyl's escape, the vessel was passed on the starboard side, at a height
(75) of about forty feet, by a "prodigious winged creature" that witnesses among the passengers and crew described as

something between a flying goat and a monstrous bat. It was heading at terrific (80) speed in a southwesterly direction.

1. Which of the following sentences best summarizes the first paragraph?
A) Challenger conceals his unease behind an elaborate display of stagecraft.
B) Challenger prepares the audience by using showmanship to create suspense.
C) Challenger risks his reputation by exposing a terrible truth that the scientists deny.
D) Challenger calms the audience's fears by taking things step by step.

2. As it is used in line 12, "inscribed" most nearly means
A) written.
B) emblazoned.
C) listed.
D) branded.

3. It can reasonably be inferred from line 16 that the Professor
A) thinks the packing case contains a parrot.
B) usually finds the creature easy to manage.
C) has no experience with this creature.
D) is deliberately misleading the audience.

4. As it is used in line 25, "malign" most nearly means
A) vivid.
B) morbid.
C) outdated.
D) wicked.

5. The author uses lines 32–34 to convey
A) an accurate and detailed description of the creature.
B) an impression of the horror that the creature provoked.
C) a teasing apprehension of terror that makes the reader read on.
D) evidence of the writer's wide experience and scholarship.

6. As it is used in line 65, "sparse" most nearly means
A) unconvincing.
B) meager.
C) pessimistic.
D) scattered.

7. The author indicates that reported sightings of the pterodactyl
A) offer no conclusive evidence of where it went.
B) are contradictory and unreliable.
C) prove that Challenger was telling the truth.
D) show it was alive when last seen.

8. Which choice provides the best evidence for the answer to the previous question?
A) Lines 63–64 ('Nothing . . . pterodactyl")
B) Lines 64–65 ("Reports . . . sparse")
C) Lines 68–79 ("The only . . . bat")
D) Lines 73–80 ("the vessel . . . direction")

9. The description of a "prodigious winged creature" in lines 75–76 helps convey the idea that
A) the creature flew back home.
B) nobody has seen such a creature before.
C) its location will remain an unsolved mystery.
D) the creature appears mythical.

10. Which of the following sentences best summarizes the passage?
A) An escaped pterodactyl, brought to London by a professor, disappears into the skies over London.
B) A professor brings a pterodactyl into an academic meeting, where the audience panics and runs.
C) A famous explorer aims to prove that he has been to a place frozen in the Jurassic Era by bringing a captive pterodactyl to a meeting of the Royal Society in London.
D) London panics as an unidentified creature escapes from a packing case and perches for hours on Queens Hall.

Synonyms

*From the word bank below, choose the word that has the same or nearly the same meaning as the **boldface** word in each sentence and write it on the line. You will not use all of the words.*

adieu	flippant	momentous	rabid
apex	incredulous	monologue	sparse
candid	inscribe	perilous	sprightly
dross	institute	preposterous	surly

1. The student is preparing a portfolio to present as part of his application for a scholarship to the art **academy**. _____

2. The grass is newly seeded, so it is still **thin** and light in color. _____

3. For many serious runners, completing a marathon represents the **peak** of achievement. _____

4. At one time, the idea of a self-driving car would have seemed **absurd**, but today it is becoming a reality. _____

5. The Jack Russell Terrier is a particularly **peppy** breed of dog and consequently needs plenty of exercise. _____

6. Unfortunately, there was nothing to read in the waiting room except gossip magazines and other printed **trash**. _____

7. I was **mistrustful** when I first heard about double rainbows, but after doing a bit of research, I was convinced that they do, in fact, exist. _____

8. The play begins with an unconventional scene in which each of the main characters delivers a **soliloquy** directly to the audience. _____

9. It was emotionally difficult for the doctor to say her **good-bye** to the colleagues and staff she had worked with for such a long time. _____

10. A politician with a **cranky** and dismissive manner has little chance of being elected. _____

11. Instead of your flattery, I would appreciate your **sincere** opinion of my stories. _____

12. People who do **hazardous** jobs deserve our respect. _____

Two-Word Completions

Select the pair of words that best completes the meaning of each of the following sentences.

1. "Over the years, consumer prices have soared, while the real purchasing power of the dollar has _____," the speaker said. "If the cost of living continues to _____, the value of our money must surely shrink even more."
   - **a.** escalated . . . dwindle
   - **b.** dwindled . . . escalate
   - **c.** dwindled . . . dwindle
   - **d.** escalated . . . escalate

2. Some people really enjoy doing all the tiresome and time-consuming chores associated with housework, but to me such _____ is truly _____.
   - **a.** assurance . . . pensive
   - **b.** liability . . . grievous
   - **c.** immunity . . . obstreperous
   - **d.** drudgery . . . repugnant

3. Roman governors had at their command both regular legionary troops and _____ units drawn from the native population to repel the _____ of savage barbarians that from time to time swarmed into the provinces of the Empire like an invasion of locusts.
   - **a.** heterogeneous . . . envoys
   - **b.** pugnacious . . . tirades
   - **c.** auxiliary . . . hordes
   - **d.** vagrant . . . realms

4. After fighting my way all year along the noisy, crowded streets of a bustling modern _____ like Tokyo or New York, I find it quite a pleasure to _____ aimlessly along a winding country road.
   - **a.** metropolis . . . meander
   - **b.** cubicle . . . venture
   - **c.** realm . . . dilate
   - **d.** asylum . . . impel

5. Does the old saying, "Nothing _____, nothing gained," mean that someone who expects to be _____ well for his or her efforts must be prepared to take some risks?
   - **a.** feigned . . . impelled
   - **b.** scuttled . . . maligned
   - **c.** assimilated . . . inundated
   - **d.** ventured . . . remunerated

6. "They're asking far too much for this _____ merchandise," I remarked. "I'd be a fool to pay such a(n) _____ price for goods that are so badly made."
   - **a.** grievous ... auxiliary
   - **b.** shoddy . . . exorbitant
   - **c.** sterling ... expedient
   - **d.** bogus ... rasping

7. As soon as the robins and the crocuses herald the _____ of spring, our personnel department is _____ with a veritable deluge of letters from college students asking about summer employment.
   - **a.** flair ... consoled
   - **b.** interim ... impelled
   - **c.** advent . . . inundated
   - **d.** prognosis ... rejuvenated

Idioms

In the passage about pests in urban areas (see pages 100–101), the author says, "With so many pests to keep at bay, keeping our homes and cities clean remains a momentous task."

"Keep at bay" is an idiom that means "keep a safe distance away" or "stop something troublesome from getting too close." An **idiom** is an informal expression that cannot be translated literally; its actual meaning is often quite different from the literal meanings of its words. Idioms often rely on figures of speech, or imaginative comparisons, as in the phrase "the apple of my eye." The meaning of an idiom may not be obvious or self-evident, so idioms must be learned, just like any new or unfamiliar vocabulary.

Choosing the Right Idiom

Read each sentence. Use context clues to figure out the meaning of each idiom in **boldface***. Then write the letter of the definition for the idiom in the sentence.*

1. It's a **toss up** between who is a better soccer player, my brother or me._____

2. My sister, who is a real **goody two-shoes**, follows every rule to the letter._____

3. It's **a blessing in disguise** that no one wanted to play ball, as there were strong thunderstorms today._____

4. I thought my friend was really hurt, but he was just **crying wolf**._____

5. The lead part in the play was won by **a dark horse**—that quiet, shy new girl from Boston._____

6. My real fear is that when my friends find out about my encounter with an angry duck, they will have **a field day** making fun of me._____

7. My cousin dragged me to a comic book convention, where I felt like a real **fish out of water**._____

8. If I **go out on a limb** and hire you, you will need to prove to me that I made a good choice._____

9. Diets that claim to help people lose weight quickly are **a dime a dozen**._____

10. Unfortunately, the gerbil we bought for my sister **kicked the bucket** only a week after we brought it home.

_____

a. easily available; extremely common

b. a really good time

c. an unexpected contender

d. died

e. something that reveals itself to be a good thing after the fact

f. person who is smugly obedient and zealously conforms to the rules

g. an even chance

h. asking for help or attention without really needing it

i. someone who feels out of place

j. take a risk

Classical Roots

pol—city, state
ly—to loosen, to set free

The root *pol* appears in **metropolis**, "a large city" (page 102). The root *ly* appears in **catalyst**, "any agent that causes change" (page 70). Some other words based on these roots are listed below.

acropolis	cosmopolitan	metropolitan	political
analysis	electrolysis	paralysis	psychoanalysis

From the list of words above, choose the one that corresponds to each of the brief definitions below. Write the word in the blank space in the illustrative sentence below the definition. Use an online or print dictionary if necessary.

1. relating to a major city; comprised of a central city and its adjacent suburbs
Most _____ newspapers include arts and entertainment listings.

2. involving politicians, governmental organizations, or parties on distinct sides in an issue
When I vote, I align myself with a particular _____ party.

3. the fortified upper part or citadel of an ancient Greek city
While in Greece, we visited the "Sacred Rock of Athens" to see the ruins of the ancient _____.

4. decomposition of an electrolyte caused by electric current passing through it; removal of excess hair or other tissue by destroying it with a needlelike electrode
In 1869, Doctor Charles Michel first practiced _____ when he sent a current through a gold needle to remove a swollen ingrown eyelash.

5. common to or representative of the whole world; at home everywhere, widespread; conversant with many spheres of interest
Music is truly a _____ art form.

6. partial or complete loss, or temporary interruption, of the ability to move or experience sensation in part or all of the body; any condition of helpless inactivity or powerlessness
A serious spinal cord injury can result in permanent _____.

7. the breaking apart of a complex whole into its simpler parts for closer study; a statement of the results of this process; a brief summary or outline
Chemical _____ of the debris can establish the fire's cause.

8. a therapeutic examination of the mind, developed by Freud, to discover the unconscious desires, fears, and anxieties that produce mental and emotional disorders; psychiatric treatment based on this theory and its methodology
The man will undergo _____ to cure his depression.

*Read the following passage, taking note of the **boldface** words and their contexts. These words are among those you will be studying in Unit 10. It may help you to complete the exercises in this Unit if you refer to the way the words are used below.*

Remarkable Mixes
<Textbook Entry>

A zorse is a hybrid of a zebra and a horse.

Hybrid Animals

A hybrid animal is born of parents of related but different species. About ten percent of all animal species naturally engage in interbreeding that produces offspring. Sometimes these hybrid offspring fill a biological niche that is not in competition with its parent species for survival. As a result, a distinct third species evolves.

Man-made Hybrids

It is **erroneous** to regard hybrid animals solely as the outcome of natural pairings. Some hybrids develop when people **aspire** to "build a better mousetrap." The following animals are examples of species interbred for human use:

a) Beefalo are the offspring of domestic cattle and American bison.[1] Beefalo meat is lower in fat, calories, and cholesterol than lean beef.

b) The cama is a hybrid that blends the strength, size, and endurance of a camel[2] with the sure-footed and more **diminutive** llama.[3]

c) The mule is a hardy cross between a horse and a donkey. The mule is **adept** in **rugged** terrain. It will navigate narrow passages and steep trails at a **languid** but sure-footed pace.

Interbreeding for Survival

Because climate change and overdevelopment threaten animals' natural habitats, prospects are **bleak** for the long-term survival of some species. However, evidence of interbreeding gives scientists hope. One example of such interbreeding is the grolar—part polar bear,[4] part grizzly bear.[5] This blend occurs rarely but naturally, where polar bears have left

---

[1] a large bovine with short horns and large shoulders that occurs naturally in North America
[2] a large mammal native to Asian and African deserts, frequently used as a mount and pack animal
[3] a relative of the camel, smaller and native to South America, used for its wool and as a pack animal

the ice to roam the land with grizzlies. Grolars resemble both parents. The hairy feet of a polar bear are ideally suited for the landscape where it lives, **rendering** the stark, Arctic tundra habitable. The hairy soles of a grolar's feet, coupled with its grizzlylike claws and humped back, made **skeptical** observers wonder whether to call this creature a polar bear or a grizzly bear. DNA testing gave **invincible** proof that the grolar had one parent of each bear. The grolar may signal a new kind of bear. Its mixed traits can help it adapt to changes in climate and habitat.

Health

When a hybrid is an improvement over its parents, it is said to have the advantage of hybrid vigor. An example of hybrid vigor is Hercules—a 900-pound, 12-foot-long liger. This cat was naturally born to a female tiger and a male lion in an American wildlife sanctuary. Hercules is strong, healthy, playful, and intelligent, though the long-term effects of this hybridization have not been studied. Not all hybrids, including other ligers, are as successful as Hercules, as interbreeding can **impair** health. Some hybrids are sickly, sterile, or short-lived.

A liger is a cross between a tiger and a lion.

Ethical Concerns

Critics regard the planned interbreeding of species as a **despicable** act of arrogance borne of **slipshod** ethics. They **chide** breeders for **exploiting** already vulnerable species. The critics' concern is that endangered species may disappear not by extinction, but by the misdirected experimentation of science.

Whether hybrids are natural or man-made, their attempts to survive have fascinated humans for centuries. As genetic testing becomes more widespread and sophisticated, it is likely that new hybrids will be discovered among animals previously thought to be a separate species.

The mule is one of the best-known hybrid animals.

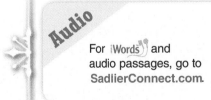

For iWords and audio passages, go to SadlierConnect.com.

---

[4] a large, white bear native to polar regions

[5] a large, brown bear native to the United States and Canadian Northwest

Definitions

Note the spelling, pronunciation, part(s) of speech, and definition(s) of each of the following words. Then write the appropriate form of the word in the blank space in the illustrative sentence(s) following.

1. adept
(*adj.,* ə dept'; *n.,* a' dept)

(*adj.*) thoroughly skilled; (*n.*) an expert
Not only is the soloist an accomplished singer, but he is also _____ at playing the saxophone.
An _____ at chess, she hopes to compete in tournaments against top-rated players.

2. chide
(chīd)

(*v.*) to blame; scold
The teacher _____ the student for truancy and tardiness.

3. despicable
(di spik' ə bəl)

(*adj.*) worthy of scorn, contemptible
Whatever the provocation, there is no justification for such _____ behavior.

4. erroneous
(e rō' nē əs)

(*adj.*) incorrect, containing mistakes
An _____ first impression is not easily corrected.

5. exploit
(*v.,* ek sploit'; *n.,* ek' sploit)

(*v.*) to make use of, develop; to make improper use of for personal profit; (*n.*) a feat, deed
A good debater knows how to _____ weaknesses in an opponent's argument.
The _____ of Robin Hood and his Merry Men are so well known that they have become a part of Western culture.

6. impair
(im pâr')

(*v.*) to make imperfect, damage, harm
I am fortunate that the scratch on my eye will not permanently _____ my vision.

7. languid
(laŋ' gwid)

(*adj.*) drooping; without energy, sluggish
A big lunch makes me feel _____ for the rest of the day.

8. render
(ren' dər)

(*v.*) to cause to become; to perform; to deliver officially; to process, extract
The freelance writer presented the managing editor with a bill for services _____.

9. skeptical
(skep' tə kəl)

(*adj.*) inclined to doubt; slow to accept something as true

I am _____ of promises made by politicians when they are running for office.

10. slipshod
(slip' shäd)

(*adj.*) untidy in dress, personal habits, etc.; careless, sloppy

The commission attributed the unfortunate collapse of the apartment building to its _____ construction.

Using Context

*For each item, determine whether the **boldface** word from pages 146–147 makes sense in the context of the sentence. Circle the item numbers next to the six sentences in which the words are used correctly.*

1. Some wildlife experts know how to use their bare hands to **render** an alligator harmless and then capture it.

2. The soft, soothing lullaby will **chide** the children to sleep.

3. Deliberately dumping pollutants and waste into a lake or a river is a **despicable** act.

4. Now that I have seen the movie, I am completely **skeptical** about it and would definitely recommend it to others.

5. The basketball players' **erroneous** passes at yesterday's game delighted not only their coach, but their fans as well.

6. The whipping winds and swirling snow will **impair** the rescuers' ability to locate the missing climbers.

7. In the years leading up to the American Revolution, many colonists complained that King George and the British government were determined to **exploit** them.

8. If you go out like that, with your hair uncombed and your shoelaces untied, you will look completely **slipshod**.

9. Octopuses are surprisingly **adept** at handling objects with their arms, and some have even been known to use them to open jars.

10. The diamond looks dull and rough now, but once it is cut and polished, it will be sparkling and **languid**.

Choosing the Right Word

*Select the **boldface** word that better completes each sentence. You might refer to the passage on pages 144–145 to see how most of these words are used in context. Note that the choices might be related forms of the Unit words.*

1. After four years as the President's press secretary, I have become a noted (**adept, exploit**) in the art of fielding questions.

2. The artist, who had trained as an architect, (**rendered, impaired**) a realistic drawing of the hotel lobby that was nearly as detailed as a photograph.

3. Sergei (**chided, exploited**) Natasha's love for him by asking for a favor.

4. The visitor's huge bulk, combined with his (**skeptical, languid**) manner, made me think of a tired whale.

5. I am not accusing anyone of deliberately lying, but I can prove beyond doubt that the charges are (**adept, erroneous**).

6. The goalie's reflexes were as sharp as ever, but the knee injury had plainly (**impaired, chided**) her ability to maneuver.

7. I would never trust my funds to anyone who is so (**adept, slipshod**) in managing his own affairs.

8. It is worse than useless to (**render, chide**) children for misbehaving without giving them an opportunity to behave better.

9. Rita, who until a year ago had never prepared anything more complicated than scrambled eggs, is now quite an (**adept, erroneous**) cook.

10. A good scientist will always be (**skeptical, despicable**) about any theory that is not backed by convincing evidence.

11. That monologue about the young accountant on his very first day on the job (**rendered, exploited**) me helpless with laughter.

12. Far from admiring the way they got those letters of recommendation, I consider their deception utterly (**skeptical, despicable**).

Completing the Sentence

Choose the word from the word bank that best completes each of the following sentences. Write the correct word or form of the word in the space provided.

adept	despicable	exploit	languid	skeptical
chide	erroneous	impair	render	slipshod

1. Why do you take it on yourself to _____ me whenever I say or do anything even slightly out of line?

2. I understand math very well, but, according to my teacher, my performance in class is, at best, _____.

3. The warmth of the June sun made me feel so _____ that I scarcely had the energy to brush away the flies.

4. Poor diet, lack of exercise, and insufficient rest have done a great deal to _____ my health.

5. The fiddler _____ the Virginia reel in a very lively fashion.

6. It is better to admit ignorance than to give _____ information.

7. The inconsistencies in the suspect's story made the police highly _____ of his alibi.

8. To improve their standard of living, the people of an underdeveloped country must learn to _____ the resources of their land.

9. The social worker said with great emphasis that anyone who would take advantage of an elderly person is utterly _____.

10. The master silversmith was extraordinarily _____ in the use of simple hand tools.

Definitions

Note the spelling, pronunciation, part(s) of speech, and definition(s) of each of the following words. Then write the appropriate form of the word in the blank space in the illustrative sentence(s) following.

1. aspire
(ə spīr')

(*v.*) to have ambitious hopes or plans, strive toward a higher goal, desire earnestly; to ascend

An early fascination with ants led the young naturalist to _____ to a career as an entomologist.

2. bleak
(blēk)

(*adj.*) bare, dreary, dismal

Urban renewal can turn a run-down city with _____ economic prospects into a flourishing metropolis.

3. diminutive
(də min' yə tiv)

(*adj.*) small, smaller than most others of the same type

The _____ lapdog was so small that it actually fit in its owner's purse.

4. emancipate
(ēman' sə pāt)

(*v.*) to free from slavery; to release or liberate

Scientific knowledge can _____ humanity from blind superstition.

5. extemporaneous
(ek stem pə rā' nē əs)

(*adj.*) made or delivered on the spur of the moment

The stand-up comedian's outrageous act included about twenty minutes of completely _____ banter.

6. invincible
(in vin' sə bəl)

(*adj.*) not able to be defeated, unbeatable

Napoleon I, emperor of France, was _____ until he launched a disastrous invasion of Russia.

7. mire
(mīr)

(*n.*) mud; wet, swampy ground; a tough situation; (*v.*) to get stuck

The once verdant expanse of the soccer field has become a rectangle of muck and _____.

Congress will never ratify that bill _____ in controversy.

8. obtrusive
(əb trü' siv)

(*adj.*) forward; undesirably prominent; thrust out

I don't blame you for being put off by his _____ attempt to dominate the conversation.

9. preamble
(prē' am bəl)

(*n.*) an introduction to a speech or piece of writing

The _____ to the Constitution describes the purpose of our national government.

10. rugged
(rəg' əd)

(*adj.*) rough, irregular; severe, stern; strong; stormy

Settlers had a rough time crossing the _____ Appalachian Mountains.

Using Context

*For each item, determine whether the **boldface** word from pages 150–151 makes sense in the context of the sentence. Circle the item numbers next to the six sentences in which the words are used correctly.*

1. As a **preamble**, the CEO thanked the staff members for their hard work before launching into her speech.

2. Developments in technology over the last century have helped to **emancipate** many workers from tedious manual labor.

3. My mother's **diminutive** sense of fashion leads many people to believe that she is younger than she actually is.

4. Even experienced mountain climbers should be cautious on **rugged** terrain to avoid slipping and injuring themselves.

5. The garden, with its dried-up grass and dead plants, looked **bleak** and neglected.

6. The entire school believed our football team to be **invincible** until they lost the final game of the season.

7. He had never seen the ocean before and was enthralled with the vast **mire** before him.

8. The **obtrusive** questions asked by the audience members sparked insightful discussions among the panel members.

9. Those who **aspire** to become doctors should focus not only on studying science, but also on how to display compassion.

10. The **extemporaneous** nature of the question-and-answer session boosted the confidence of the participants.

Choosing the Right Word

*Select the **boldface** word that better completes each sentence. You might refer to the passage on pages 144–145 to see how most of these words are used in context. Note that the choices might be related forms of the Unit words.*

1. In Jonathan Swift's fictional country of Lilliput, everyone and everything is pint-sized, or (**diminutive, obtrusive**).

2. I could see that the merchant's long, sad story about bad luck was only the (**mire, preamble**) to a request for a loan.

3. When I asked the student why she wasn't going to the senior prom, she answered only with a(n) (**bleak, obtrusive**) smile.

4. After enslaved African-Americans were (**mired, emancipated**), many emigrated to northern states to start new lives.

5. The sculptor has done a superb job of representing the strong, rough planes of the leader's (**bleak, rugged**) features.

6. Passengers could not exit the bus without tripping over the (**invincible, obtrusive**) package in the aisle.

7. Just as in fairy tales, the way to Grandma's house was a long, winding, and (**diminutive, rugged**) path through dark woods.

8. Our basketball team, with its well-planned attack, tight defense, and seven-foot center, proved all but (**invincible, bleak**) .

9. When Emerson said, "Hitch your wagon to a star," he meant that we should (**aspire, mire**) to reach the very highest levels of which we are capable.

10. When we tried to straighten out the mess, we found ourselves (**mired, emancipated**) in a mass of inaccurate, incomplete, and mixed-up records.

11. In the (**obtrusive, extemporaneous**) give-and-take of a televised debate, it is easy for a nervous nominee to make a slip of the tongue.

12. It is up to all of us to (**aspire, emancipate**) ourselves from prejudices and false ideas acquired early in life.

Completing the Sentence

Choose the word from the word bank that best completes each of the following sentences. Write the correct word or form of the word in the space provided.

aspire	diminutive	extemporaneous	mire	preamble
bleak	emancipate	invincible	obtrusive	rugged

1. The honoree's after-dinner speech was so polished and sure that we never guessed that it was _____.

2. We learned that the matchless discipline and superior leadership of the Roman legions made them all but _____.

3. Marching over the _____ terrain under a broiling sun, we were soon on the verge of exhaustion.

4. The _____ but powerful halfback from Syracuse was one of the lightest men ever to play professional football.

5. How can you _____ to work in the space program when you haven't even been able to pass your science and math courses?

6. Before we get into the specific details of our proposal, we should write a(n) _____ that will explain in general terms what we want to do.

7. Against the solemn hush of the memorial service, the boisterous laughter we heard was _____.

8. There are millions of people throughout the world still waiting to be _____ from the bonds of grinding poverty.

9. The Welsh mining village, with its rows of drab cottages, seemed terribly _____ and uninviting in the cold autumn rain.

10. Since it had rained all night, the newly-plowed fields were now an impassable _____.

Synonyms

*Choose the word or form of the word from this Unit that is the same or most nearly the same in meaning as the **boldface** word or expression in the phrase. Write that word on the line. Use a dictionary if necessary.*

1. wallow like an alligator in the **marsh** _____
2. the **unconquerable** warrior _____
3. a **vile** and cowardly act _____
4. an **adroit** musician _____
5. **unshackle** a person from bondage _____
6. the **miniature** poodle _____
7. **impromptu** speech on a humorous topic _____
8. contained **fallacious** information _____
9. **dubious** about the chances of winning _____
10. **mar** relations between nations _____
11. the opening remarks, or **preface** _____
12. an accusation that **made** him speechless _____
13. not just assertive, but **impudent** _____
14. **yearn** to be an Olympic champion _____
15. **utilize** natural resources _____

Antonyms

*Choose the word or form of the word from this Unit that is most nearly opposite in meaning to the **boldface** word or expression in the phrase. Write that word on the line. Use a dictionary if necessary.*

1. the **smooth** terrain _____
2. feeling **energetic** after a day at the shore _____
3. a **careful and thorough** repair job _____
4. **praised** for their actions _____
5. had a **sunny** outlook _____

Writing: Words in Action

Is it unethical to interbreed species for human use? Should animal hybrids be the result of natural pairings? In a brief essay, explore the benefits and drawbacks of both kinds of animal hybrids. Use at least two details from the passage (pages 144–145) and three or more words from this Unit to support your choice.

Vocabulary in Context

*Some of the words you have studied in this Unit appear in **boldface** type. Read the passage below, and then circle the letter of the correct answer for each word as it is used in context.*

Hybrid creatures are prominent in numerous myths from cultures around the world. In Greek mythology, for example, some of the most colorful hybrids are the centaurs, half horse and half human. Centaurs are usually portrayed as rowdy, dangerous creatures, but Chiron is a notable exception. Chiron is a perfect example of wisdom and kindness, whose patient teaching did much to **emancipate** his students from the **mire** of ignorance. These pupils included Achilles, hero of the Trojan War and Chiron's own great-grandson, and Asclepius, the god of healing. Accidentally wounded by a poisoned arrow shot by the hero Heracles, Chiron gave up his own immortality in favor of Prometheus, the great benefactor of humanity.

Such an uplifting **preamble** could hardly introduce the mythical hybrids called Harpies. Vulture-like creatures with the heads of women, Harpies had long, curved claws—**obtrusive** appendages, but appropriate because the name harpies means "snatchers" or "grabbers" in Greek. Ugly and misshapen, Harpies were associated with storm winds and also with the underworld. The Greco-Roman myths most often depicted Harpies as cruel predators.

No hybrid creature confronted its victims with as **bleak** a fate as the Sphinx. Composed of a lion's body, a bird's wings, and a human head, the Sphinx was known in Egypt as early as 2500 BCE. A thousand years later, it occurred in Mesopotamia. The most famous Sphinx of all was that of Greek mythology, who was said to terrorize everyone she encountered by demanding an **extemporaneous** answer to her riddle: What is it that walks on all fours and then becomes two-footed and three-footed? Only the hero Oedipus was able to escape destruction by giving the correct answer: a human being.

1. To **emancipate** someone is to make that person
   a. skillful
   b. intelligent
   c. free
   d. grateful

2. The word **mire** most nearly means
   a. swamp
   b. ditch
   c. chaos
   d. labyrinth

3. A **preamble** is best defined as a(n)
   a. epilogue
   b. introduction
   c. summary
   d. footnote

4. A feature that is **obtrusive**
   a. sticks out
   b. changes appearance
   c. is subtle
   d. is dull

5. A **bleak** outcome might best be described as
   a. rosy
   b. magical
   c. puzzling
   d. grim

6. An **extemporaneous** answer would normally be delivered
   a. off-the-cuff
   b. in hushed tones
   c. slowly and carefully
   d. after much research

*Read the following passage, taking note of the **boldface** words and their contexts. These words are among those you will be studying in Unit 11. It may help you to complete the exercises in this Unit if you refer to the way the words are used below.*

Failing Infrastructure
<Newspaper Editorial>

Washington, D.C.—April 11

Yesterday, Concerned Citizens for Safe Infrastructure (CCSI), a national watchdog organization with headquarters in the nation's capital, released its annual report, "State of Our Infrastructure." The news was not encouraging. Petunia Hargraves, Executive Director of CCSI, did not mince words as she delivered a **concise** summary of the group's findings.

"Almost everywhere we look, public facilities have **deteriorated** badly," she said. "All levels of government must act urgently to **forestall** future damage and **depreciation** of these public assets. The costs will be substantial, but we must not **recoil** from our obligation to society."

Thirteen lives were lost when a bridge collapsed in Minneapolis.

Infrastructure, as every highway commuter inching past a construction site knows, is the basic cluster of facilities on which a city or state depends. Roads, airports, bridges, tunnels, railways, and ports: All are infrastructure.

CCSI was founded shortly after the collapse of a section of a major bridge along I-35 in Minneapolis in August 2007. That disaster claimed 13 lives and injured 145 people. Even before that incident, the Department of Transportation (DOT) **divulged** some unsettling facts about the maintenance of our nation's infrastructure.

Its numbers show that, due to neglect, millions of commuters' lives are put at risk every day. In 1971, Congress passed a **statute** requiring that all bridges be inspected every two years. Unfortunately, many states, using various loopholes in the law, have failed to **comport** with this federal regulation. Those with the worst rates of compliance are shown in the chart below.

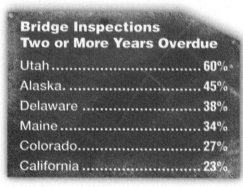

Bridge Inspections Two or More Years Overdue	
Utah	60%
Alaska	45%
Delaware	38%
Maine	34%
Colorado	27%
California	23%

The National Transportation Safety Board diagnosed the probable cause of the Minneapolis bridge collapse with striking **brevity**: "inadequate load capacity." Clearly, there are more cars on the road today than there were 40 years ago, but infrastructure has not kept pace.

"Obsolete public facilities need to be replaced," says CCSI's Hargraves. "With each incident like the I-35 bridge collapse, the public becomes more **enlightened** about the necessity for maintaining infrastructure. But people have short memories. What we have at present is a mere **rivulet** of corrective action. What we need is a torrent."

"The age of each asset is not the only risk factor," a DOT official pointed out to this reporter. "Quality, too, is important." The bridge that collapsed in Minneapolis was 40 years old, he notes, but at Charles de Gaulle Airport in Paris, the roof of a brand-new terminal caved in. That disaster, which occurred in May 2004 and killed four people, followed the terminal's grand opening by barely a year.

CCSI's Hargraves put forward an analogy from the ancient world. "It's a bad bridge that's narrower than the stream. The Romans did not ignore vital infrastructure and they did not cut corners when building," she asserted. "Their roads, bridges, theaters, and aqueducts are still with us. We should follow their example. Any other approach **reeks** of complacency."

As the world urbanizes, infrastructure needs grow at a **relentless** pace. In China, for example, **proponents** of high-speed train service have convinced the government to double the country's rail coverage by the year 2020. This ambitious goal is estimated to cost $300 billion. Some economists harbor doubts as to whether China's plan will work. The state, these critics claim, is **squandering** funds: It will not **recoup** its investment, because high-speed fares are too expensive for the average traveler.

To create an infrastructure that is truly modern, efficient, and safe, says the CCSI report, governments must not **quaver**: They should look to the values of the past while boldly building for the future.

Audio

For iWords and audio passages, go to SadlierConnect.com.

Less than a year after it was built, a Parisian airport terminal collapsed.

E12

Definitions

Note the spelling, pronunciation, part(s) of speech, and definition(s) of each of the following words. Then write the appropriate form of the word in the blank space in the illustrative sentence(s) following.

1. **brevity**
   (brev′ ə tē)

   (*n.*) shortness
   The speech was notable more for its
   _____ than for its clarity.

2. **concise**
   (kən sīs′)

   (*adj.*) expressing much in a few words
   As a rule of thumb, editors and readers appreciate
   writing that is _____ and forceful.

3. **deteriorate**
   (di tir′ ē ə rāt)

   (*v.*) to lower in quality or value; to wear away
   It is painful for anyone, particularly a doctor, to watch
   someone's health _____.

4. **enlightened**
   (en līt′ ənd)

   (*adj.*) free from ignorance and false ideas; possessing
   sound understanding
   An _____ society is ruled by knowledge
   and reason rather than superstition and prejudice.

5. **forestall**
   (fōr stôl′)

   (*v.*) to prevent by acting first
   Sometimes it is possible to _____ a
   cold by taking Vitamin C.

6. **proponent**
   (prō pō′ nənt)

   (*n.*) one who puts forward a proposal; one who supports
   a cause or belief
   Lucretia Coffin Mott and Elizabeth Cady Stanton were
   among the first _____ of women's
   suffrage in the United States.

7. **quaver**
   (kwā′ vər)

   (*v.*) to shake, tremble; to trill
   My voice _____ whenever I try to
   reach the high notes.

8. **recoup**
   (ri küp′)

   (*v.*) to make up for, regain
   I plan to _____ my family's lost fortune by
   working hard, earning extra money, and investing wisely.

9. reek
(rēk)

(*n.*) an unpleasant smell; (*v.*) to give off unpleasant smells; to give a strong impression

The unmistakable _____ of spoiled food greeted us as we entered the long-abandoned cabin.

In *How the Other Half Lives* (1890), Jacob Riis describes tenements in urban neighborhoods that _____ of poverty.

10. statute
(stach′ ŭt)

(*n.*) a law

The student body is governed by the _____ of the university.

Using Context

*For each item, determine whether the **boldface** word from pages 158–159 makes sense in the context of the sentence. Circle the item numbers next to the six sentences in which the words are used correctly.*

1. Our grandfather, a lifelong **proponent** of healthy living, encourages everyone to exercise every day.

2. Pet owners must comply with the **statute** of the town that requires every pet to be licensed.

3. A résumé is a **concise** summary of a person's educational background and work experience that is usually no longer than one or two pages.

4. Why does the kitchen **reek** of a scrumptious dinner almost ready to be served?

5. Over time, the pages of a book or newspaper will dry out and **deteriorate**.

6. Arthur Miller's play *The Crucible* focuses on a set of tragic events that occur in a community that has become intolerant and **enlightened**.

7. The candidate was sure that her strong performance in the debate would **forestall** her victory in the upcoming election.

8. The poem was a reflection on the **brevity** of life and the need to live every day to the fullest.

9. His voice might **quaver** at first, but by the end of the song he will sound strong and steady.

10. The illness robbed the athlete of her energy, causing her to **recoup** her strength and withdraw from the tournament.

Choosing the Right Word

*Select the **boldface** word that better completes each sentence. You might refer to the passage on pages 156–157 to see how most of these words are used in context. Note that the choices might be related forms of the Unit words.*

1. William Shakespeare expressed the tragic (**brevity, statute**) of life by comparing it to a candle that must soon go out.

2. An old Chinese proverb suggests: "Make a candle to get light; read a book to get (**enlightened, concise**)."

3. Once a political leader has lost the confidence of voters, it is almost impossible to (**forestall, recoup**) it.

4. In spite of the vast number of details in the United States Constitution, the document is remarkably (**enlightened, concise**).

5. When I learned how the air and water were being polluted, I became a strong (**brevity, proponent**) of ecological reforms.

6. To (**recoup, forestall**) criticism of my proposal, I prepared for the meeting by gathering relevant facts and figures beforehand.

7. After the huge fire burned down several houses in our area, the air was filled with ashes and the (**proponent, reek**) of acrid smoke.

8. It's all very well to build new housing, but we should also rehabilitate neighborhoods that have (**deteriorated, quavered**) through neglect.

9. I wish there were a (**proponent, statute**) that would prevent people from revealing the ending of a detective story!

10. She tried to appear calm, but her voice (**quavered, deteriorated**), revealing her agitation.

11. (**Statutes, Proponents**) of the new youth soccer league met with the local parents to discuss by-laws, safety rules, uniforms, and other pressing issues.

12. It's not surprising that the clothing of firefighters often (**quavers, reeks**) of smoke and sweat.

Completing the Sentence

Choose the word from the word bank that best completes each of the following sentences. Write the correct word or form of the word in the space provided.

brevity	deteriorate	forestall	quaver	reek
concise	enlightened	proponent	recoup	statute

1. It's up to us to work twice as hard to _____ our losses now that the storm has damaged the crops.

2. The program featured a debate between _____ of gun control and critics of legislation restricting ownership of firearms.

3. Since you are charged for every word you use in the advertisement, it pays to be as _____ as possible.

4. A President will often try to _____ the defeat of a legislative program by appealing for the public's support on TV.

5. What we need is not a lot of new legislation, but tough enforcement of the _____ already on the books.

6. "I'm not afraid of anyone!" the girl piped up bravely, but we noticed that her voice _____ as she said it.

7. A(n) _____ public opinion, said Jefferson, is essential to a democratic society.

8. The telltale _____ of gas alerted us that someone had left a burner open on the stove.

9. In saying that "_____ is the soul of wit," Shakespeare was reminding comedians to keep their jokes short and snappy.

10. Despite the creature comforts we now enjoy, I feel that the quality of life has somehow _____ in recent years.

Definitions

Note the spelling, pronunciation, part(s) of speech, and definition(s) of each of the following words. Then write the appropriate form of the word in the blank space in the illustrative sentence(s) following.

1. **comport**
   (kəm pôrt′)

   (*v.*) to conduct or bear oneself, behave; to be in agreement
   As the students started to leave, the principal reminded them to _____ themselves as school emissaries.

2. **demure**
   (di myür′)

   (*adj.*) sober or serious in manner, modest
   Despite her _____ appearance, she is a competitive speed skater, always ready for a challenge on ice.

3. **depreciation**
   (di prē shē ā′ shən)

   (*n.*) a lessening in value; a belittling
   The accountant calculated the _____ of the computer over a period of five years.

4. **divulge**
   (di vəlj′)

   (*v.*) to tell, reveal; to make public
   On some occasions, scrupulous reporters cannot _____ their sources of information.

5. **garble**
   (gär′ bəl)

   (*v.*) to distort in such a way as to make unintelligible
   If you've played "telephone," you know how easy it is to inadvertently _____ a message.

6. **recoil**
   (*v.*, ri koil′;
   n., rē′ koil)

   (*v.*) to spring back, shrink; (*n.*) the act of springing back
   In "The Adventure of the Speckled Band," sleuth Sherlock Holmes points out that "violence does, in truth, _____ upon the violent."
   When the engineer accidentally released the giant spring, its powerful _____ sent him sprawling.

7. **relentless**
   (ri lent′ ləs)

   (*adj.*) unyielding, harsh, without pity
   The novel *Les Misérables* recounts ex-convict Jean Valjean's lifelong flight from a _____ police inspector.

8. **rivulet**
   (riv′ yü lət)

   (*n.*) a small stream
   While we could hear the running water, dense vegetation hid the _____ from view.

9. squander
(skwän′ dər)

(*v.*) to spend foolishly, waste

I think that it is criminal to _____ our natural resources.

10. staccato
(stə kät′ ō)

(*adj.*) detached or disconnected in sound or style

We strained to listen, and we heard _____ hoofbeats striking the pavement.

Using Context

*For each item, determine whether the **boldface** word from pages 162–163 makes sense in the context of the sentence. Circle the item numbers next to the six sentences in which the words are used correctly.*

1. Although airplanes are now the preferred method of transatlantic travel for most passengers, ships are still a useful way to **comport** cargo.

2. Despite how tired I was, the **staccato** barking of neighborhood dogs kept me awake for hours.

3. The **recoil** of the crowd during the concert was so loud that we could hardly hear the band we had all come to see.

4. My sister, a social butterfly, was acting unusually **demure** during the party.

5. The train's speaker system was known to **garble** the conductor's announcements so badly that passengers had to listen intently or they would miss their stops.

6. I like to sit beside the ocean and watch each wave **divulge** out from the sea.

7. The heat was so intense that as soon as I stepped outside, a **rivulet** of sweat began to stream down my forehead.

8. It is good practice to **squander** a percentage of what you earn and set it aside for an emergency situation.

9. We were surprised that the **depreciation** of the once-popular toys was so great that we would earn almost nothing after selling our collection.

10. We thought we could have a picnic when the storm let up, but the **relentless** rainfall caused us to postpone our plans until another day.

Choosing the Right Word

*Select the **boldface** word that better completes each sentence. You might refer to the passage on pages 156–157 to see how most of these words are used in context. Note that the choices might be related forms of the Unit words.*

1. I beseeched the employees at the florist's shop to (**divulge, comport**) the name of the person who had anonymously sent me flowers, but they refused.

2. He was not surprised that the recession had affected the value of his comic book and action figure collections, resulting in their (**depreciation, rivulet**).

3. A person accused of a crime is not obliged to (**divulge, garble**) anything that might be incriminating.

4. Early rifles had such a "kick" to them that inexperienced soldiers were often injured by the (**recoil, depreciation**) after pulling the trigger.

5. (**Rivulets, Recoils**) of sweat ran down my face as I worked in that terrible heat.

6. Seeing my childhood friend so gray and infirm, I became keenly aware of the (**relentless, demure**) passage of the years.

7. "Wear and tear" is the (**depreciation, rivulet**) that results from ordinary use, not from misuse.

8. I'm not saying that you shouldn't watch television, but why (**recoil, squander**) so much of your time on those inane programs?

9. The young woman's (**demure, staccato**) smile and flirtatious manner drew admiring glances.

10. In an attempt to mislead the enemy, the crafty prisoner of war deliberately (**divulged, garbled**) his account of how the attack had been planned.

11. The speaker's (**demure, staccato**) delivery truly reminded us of a jackhammer breaking up concrete.

12. The charitable programs sponsored by this organization (**squander, comport**) well with our conception of a just and compassionate society.

Completing the Sentence

Choose the word from the word bank that best completes each of the following sentences. Write the correct word or form of the word in the space provided.

comport	depreciation	garble	relentless	squander
demure	divulge	recoil	rivulet	staccato

1. Leaders are judged by how well they _____ themselves in times of crisis.

2. As it wound its way through the desert, the mighty river became a mere _____ that travelers could easily wade across.

3. In a passage that a composer has marked _____, every note should sound like the quick thrust of a knife.

4. The child _____ in fear and disgust as the harmless water snake slithered over the floor.

5. The witnesses have testified at great length, but how much really valuable information have they _____ to the investigating committee?

6. To the district attorney's dismay, the witness _____ all the facts and misled the jury.

7. Since you worked so long and hard for the money you earned, it's doubly foolish to _____ it on things you don't really want or need.

8. How often have we heard candidates for public office promise that they will be tough and _____ in fighting organized crime!

9. Economists will tell you that inflation results in an increase in the supply of money and a(n) _____ in its value.

10. The assertive heroines portrayed in many movies are a far cry from the _____ young ladies depicted in nineteenth-century novels.

Synonyms

*Choose the word or form of the word from this Unit that is the same or most nearly the same in meaning as the **boldface** word or expression in the phrase. Write that word on the line. Use a dictionary if necessary.*

1. a **runnel** of salt water   _____
2. would not **disclose** the location   _____
3. an **ordinance** passed by the legislature   _____
4. the **devaluation** of currency   _____
5. a vocal **supporter** of civil rights   _____
6. **scramble** a radio message   _____
7. the **unremitting** persecution of Huguenots   _____
8. **thwart** an attack   _____
9. **deport oneself** with dignity   _____
10. a **disjointed** style of speech   _____
11. **pulled back** in fear   _____
12. the **stench** of decomposition   _____
13. a **diffident** and tentative reaction to strangers _____
14. **quiver** with emotion   _____
15. value **conciseness** in a short story   _____

Antonyms

*Choose the word or form of the word from this Unit that is most nearly opposite in meaning to the **boldface** word or expression in the phrase. Write that word on the line. Use a dictionary if necessary.*

1. likely to **improve** with age   _____
2. an **ignorant** electorate   _____
3. **saved** a fortune   _____
4. **lost** their initial investment   _____
5. a **long-winded** report   _____

Writing: Words in Action

How important is maintaining infrastructure as compared to other priorities, such as education, defense, and health care? In a brief essay, use examples from your reading (refer to pages 156–157), personal experience, and prior knowledge to support your point of view. Use three or more words from this Unit.

Vocabulary in Context

*Some of the words you have studied in this Unit appear in **boldface** type. Read the passage below, and then circle the letter of the correct answer for each word as it is used in context.*

The benefits of carless cities seem indisputable. The negative impacts of cars in cities exist on many levels: economic, social, and environmental. The **staccato** sounds of horns, screeching tires, and grinding gears assault the ears day and night. Signs regulating vehicular traffic **garble** the landscape. Whole neighborhoods, some with **depreciated** values, have deteriorated into strip malls. Pollution threatens the health of millions of city dwellers.

Certain trends, though, signify that America's love affair with cars may be coming to an end. The number of carless households has doubled in the past 20 years. Young people aged 25 to 34 years are moving in disproportionate numbers to transit-friendly cities and choosing not to own a car.

Still, the **proponents** of carless cities can scarcely afford to settle into **demure** complacency. Achieving the goal of more walkable, livable city spaces will require strategic planning and vigorous advocacy. Massive new investments in public transit will be needed. Most challenging of all, city planners must study and analyze a variety of models from around the world to determine which projects and strategies best **comport** with their goals. As the world urbanizes more and more rapidly, how are planners in Tokyo or London, in Venice or Zürich, maintaining the quality of life?

Planners must take the lessons learned from global surveys and apply them selectively here at home to forestall failure or disappointment. The most promising focus of attention would seem to be mid-sized cities such as Boston or Cincinnati, rather than urban giants like Los Angeles and Houston. Finally, planners must develop persuasive, specific models for commercial deliveries, emergency care, and law enforcement protection.

---

1. Noises are described as **staccato** if they sound
 a. abrupt
 b. detached
 c. melodious
 d. foreign

2. To **garble** something is to
 a. articulate
 b. magnify
 c. distort
 d. transform

3. The word **depreciated** most nearly means
 a. enhanced
 b. devalued
 c. adorned
 d. fragmented

4. The **proponents** of a plan include its
 a. analysts
 b. advocates
 c. employees
 d. critics

5. A **demure** person might be described as
 a. optimistic
 b. skeptical
 c. resolute
 d. sedate

6. If you **comport** with someone's goals, you
 a. clash
 b. agree
 c. reconcile
 d. adjust

*Read the following passage, taking note of the **boldface** words and their contexts. These words are among those you will be studying in Unit 12. It may help you to complete the exercises in this Unit if you refer to the way the words are used below.*

Social Networks and Virtual Communication
<Debate>

Today's debate question is this one: *Does social networking lead to real friendships and true communication?*

Monique: I don't think social networking leads to great friendships or communication, and frankly, I don't understand its appeal. Why should I spend an **appreciable** amount of time every day reading tiresome chit-chat? People bragging about themselves, putting others down, assuming everyone agrees with them on every issue—their posts can be unbearable! Social networking is a **synthetic** substitute for true, person-to-person interaction. If you have real friends, you don't need to sit at home and post notes to your cyber buddies. I sometimes worry that social networking has become a **subversive** force, turning us into a nation of loners, glued to computers and unable to deal with others face-to-face.

Rafael: Such a grim picture of social networking is biased and shortsighted. Rather than **contend** that social networking is synthetic, why not see it instead as the latest step in humankind's **concerted** effort to communicate better? Written language, the postal service, telephones—are these artificial too? No, these historic developments in communication bettered people's lives and, in my more **temperate** view, the same is true of social networking. The ability to keep in touch daily with friends and relatives—and to meet new people—is a great gift. Regular online contact with people we care about won't isolate us; instead, it will make us more connected, more **humane**.

against   con

true   argue

separate

together

false

Sharing our thoughts and feelings on social networks deepens our ties with others, both those we see all the time and even those we've never met. This is true at the international level, as well. In recent years, we have seen examples of **illustrious** people all around the world using social networks to organize. Digitally connected, strangers have come together *in person* to express their demands for a better society.

Monique: Isn't it ironic that we insist on the term *social* networking when so many online conversations seem *antisocial* in tone? Cyber-bullies, for example, use their computers to harass or **maltreat** their so-called friends, and their **venomous** posts can remain online indefinitely, doing lasting damage. I also **blanch** when I see some of the information that people choose to share on their own pages. What's so "social" about expressing private thoughts and experiences so publicly? I am also concerned that **autocratic** owners of some social networking Web sites might gather information about users of their sites. Such a development would be **intolerable**. Can we be sure that our privacy is safe?

Rafael: As I **ponder** such comments, I must advise that when judging social networks, don't throw the baby out with the bath water. Wading through the long list of risks attributed to social networking by its critics proves to be a **laborious** effort. Yet such critics should at least acknowledge some of its benefits. I believe that the social networking world is a mirror of the real world. In everyday life, we try to avoid bullies and decide who our true friends are, and we must do the same when networking. Just as people sometimes act objectionably in the real world, some users will post **irreverent** or even offensive comments online. Everyone feels the need to express him or herself, and social networking sites simply give people a ready audience—and instant feedback, pro or con. Social networking is still a relatively new phenomenon. As time passes, we're bound to become more savvy as users of this medium, maximizing its advantages and avoiding its pitfalls.

Audio

For iWords and audio passages, go to SadlierConnect.com.

Definitions

Note the spelling, pronunciation, part(s) of speech, and definition(s) of each of the following words. Then write the appropriate form of the word in the blank space in the illustrative sentence(s) following.

1. autocratic
(ô tə krat′ ik)

(*adj.*) absolute in power or authority
For many years, the island was under the _____ control of a dictator.

2. blasphemy
(blas′ fə mē)

(*n.*) an act, utterance, or writing showing contempt for something sacred
Galileo was accused of _____ for asserting that the sun, and not the earth, is the center of the universe.

3. concerted
(kən sər′ tid)

(*adj.*) planned or performed in cooperation with others
Teenagers and adults, northerners and southerners alike, participated in a _____ drive to register new voters.

4. intolerable
(in täl′ ər ə bəl)

(*adj.*) unbearable
To a perfectionist, mediocrity is more than unacceptable; it is simply _____.

5. irreverent
(i rev′ ər ənt)

(*adj.*) disrespectful
The student's _____ comments show a lack of respect for people in authority.

6. laborious
(lə bôr′ ē əs)

(*adj.*) not easy, requiring hard work; hardworking
After cleaning the gutters, we moved on to the _____ task of raking and bagging the leaves.

7. maltreat
(mal trēt′)

(*v.*) to abuse, use roughly or crudely
The candidate pledged to shut down any factory or manufacturing plant found to _____ workers.

8. ponder
(pän′ dər)

(*v.*) to consider carefully, reflect on
I need time to _____ all of my options before deciding how to spend the summer.

9. subversive
(səb vər′ siv)

(adj.) intended to undermine or overthrow; (n.) one who advocates or attempts to undermine a political system

The underground movement circulated _____ pamphlets that criticized the government.

The Alien and Sedition Acts enacted in 1798 gave the U.S. president the power to deport any noncitizen deemed a _____.

10. synthetic
(sin thet′ ik)

(adj.) made or put together by people; (n.) something artificial

Sometimes only a jeweler can detect the difference between an expensive _____ gem and a natural stone.

Nylon, rayon, and polyester are all _____ that have revolutionized the textile industry.

Using Context

*For each item, determine whether the **boldface** word from pages 170–171 makes sense in the context of the sentence. Circle the item numbers next to the six sentences in which the words are used correctly.*

1. After reviewing the evidence, the jury returned to the courtroom to **ponder** its decision.

2. The company is making an effort to find a more **autocratic** way of serving its customers.

3. During the Spanish Inquisition, a person accused of **blasphemy** might be tortured or executed.

4. A barn raising is a rural tradition in which the members of a community make a **concerted** effort to help a family in need by building them a new barn.

5. Camera operators and makeup artists play important but **subversive** roles on a movie set.

6. Do not expect your bicycle to last very long if you continue to **maltreat** it.

7. Abolitionists were people who found slavery **intolerable** and, through various means, worked to put an end to it.

8. The workers raced to repair the **irreverent** pipeline before it ruptured.

9. The process of building the ancient pyramids must have been **laborious**.

10. Is rayon a natural or **synthetic** fiber?

Choosing the Right Word

*Select the **boldface** word that better completes each sentence. You might refer to the passage on pages 168–169 to see how most of these words are used in context. Note that the choices might be related forms of the Unit words.*

1. Advocates of American independence were regarded by Great Britain not as patriots, but as dangerous (**subversives, blasphemy**).

2. In a country as rich as ours, it is simply (**laborious, intolerable**) that so many people live below the poverty level.

3. Even those of us not philosophically inclined occasionally like to (**maltreat, ponder**) the meaning of life.

4. We believe that a government can be strong, resourceful, and efficient without being (**subversive, autocratic**).

5. Is it (**irreverent, synthetic**) of me to suggest that the "great man" may not be as great as he thinks he is?

6. After completing the textbook, the writer faced the (**laborious, irreverent**) job of compiling the index.

7. Computer-generated synthesizers that produce (**subversive, synthetic**) speech enable individuals who have lost their voices to disease to communicate.

8. The (**laborious, autocratic**) task the ditch-diggers undertook was not going to be finished before nightfall, in spite of their best efforts.

9. All the nations of the world must join in a(n) (**concerted, irreverent**) attack on ignorance, poverty, and disease.

10. The official policy of the school is neither to pamper students nor to (**ponder, maltreat**) them.

11. To a skeptic, who doubts everything, the absolute belief in anything is (**blasphemy, synthetic**).

12. Although the song had a cheerful tune, the authoritarian government decided that the lyrics were (**subversive, laborious**).

Completing the Sentence

Choose the word from the word bank that best completes each of the following sentences. Write the correct word or form of the word in the space provided.

autocratic	concerted	irreverent	maltreat	subversive
blasphemy	intolerable	laborious	ponder	synthetic

1. I resented the _____ manner in which she told us—without even asking for our opinion—what we should do to improve our situation.

2. Students joined with faculty in a(n) _____ effort to increase the school's involvement in community affairs.

3. "Once upon a midnight dreary, while I _____ weak and weary, Over many a quaint and curious volume of forgotten lore..."

4. Our climb up the mountain was so _____ that we had to take a long rest before starting back down.

5. Some _____ fibers are actually better than natural materials for certain purposes.

6. The suspect was charged with writing and printing pamphlets that were considered _____ by the government.

7. In 1875 New York State instituted child protection laws that made it criminal to _____ children.

8. I needed the job badly, but the working conditions in that company were so _____ that I finally had to quit.

9. Some people were amused and others were outraged by the speaker's lighthearted, _____ attitude toward the institutions of government.

10. When I said that the famous rock star was singing off-key, his devoted fans seemed to think I was guilty of _____.

Definitions

Note the spelling, pronunciation, part(s) of speech, and definition(s) of each of the following words. Then write the appropriate form of the word in the blank space in the illustrative sentence(s) following.

1. **appreciable**
(ə prē' shə bəl)

   (*adj.*) sufficient to be noticed or measured

   The injured woman lost an _____ amount of blood before the paramedics arrived.

2. **blanch**
(blanch)

   (*v.*) to remove the color from; to make or turn pale; to parboil

   Even the veteran rescue worker _____ upon seeing the crash site.

3. **brawny**
(brô' nē)

   (*adj.*) strong, muscular

   In Arthurian legend, one _____ knight after another tries to pull the sword Excalibur from the stone, but none succeeds.

4. **contend**
(kən tend')

   (*v.*) to fight, struggle; to compete; to argue

   I enjoy watching the four major tennis tournaments in which brilliant players _____ for the "grand slam" titles.

5. **humane**
(hyü mān')

   (*adj.*) kind, merciful

   The _____ legal code of Hammurabi, king of Babylonia, was ahead of its time in seeking justice for the weak and the oppressed.

6. **illustrious**
(i ləs' trē əs)

   (*adj.*) very famous, distinguished

   As a student of world politics, I would be thrilled to meet an _____ member of Parliament.

7. **lithe**
(līth)

   (*adj.*) bending easily, limber

   The burly linebacker was as _____ and agile as a ballet dancer.

8. **temperate**
(tem' pər ət)

   (*adj.*) mild, moderate

   It's impossible to have a _____ discussion with a hotheaded person.

9. **venomous**
(ven′ ə məs)

(*adj.*) poisonous; spiteful, mean
Only after we had rushed the child to the emergency room did we learn that he'd been bitten by a
_____ spider.

10. **wily**
(wī′ lē)

(*adj.*) sly, shrewd, cunning
The fur trappers of colonial North America were known to be _____ traders.

Using Context

*For each item, determine whether the **boldface** word from pages 174–175 makes sense in the context of the sentence. Circle the item numbers next to the six sentences in which the words are used correctly.*

1. To flavor your water, **blanch** it with fruit and let it sit for a while.

2. The **wily** ballerina was so graceful that I felt rigid and awkward just being in the same room as her.

3. The presidential candidate maintained a **temperate** tone even while responding to baiting and unfair questions.

4. You must agree with me and **contend** that bike riding is preferable to sitting inside and watching television on such a beautiful day.

5. He is usually such a calm person that I was surprised by how **venomous** he could be when provoked.

6. I could tell my question had caught her by surprise when she didn't answer until after an **appreciable** pause.

7. The cat was sprawled for most of the afternoon in the **illustrious** patch of sun coming through the window.

8. Soon after I started practicing yoga, I noticed that my body became more **lithe**, and I could move into complex poses more easily.

9. When the **brawny** movers arrived, I felt relieved that there would be no trouble moving the enormous armoire.

10. In his application to volunteer at the animal shelter, he wrote about his belief that every living creature deserves **humane** treatment.

Choosing the Right Word

Select the **boldface** word that better completes each sentence. You might refer to the passage on pages 168–169 to see how most of these words are used in context. Note that the choices might be related forms of the Unit words.

1. Is there any other creature in the entire world that is as graceful and (**brawny, lithe**) as the common house cat?

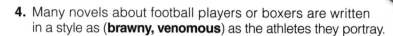

2. It's unusual to have an election in which two siblings (**blanch, contend**) for the same office.

3. He has the reputation of being a (**venomous, wily**) coach who can work with less experienced players and win.

4. Many novels about football players or boxers are written in a style as (**brawny, venomous**) as the athletes they portray.

5. When the suspect (**contended, blanched**) at the sudden accusation, her bloodless countenance as much as proclaimed her guilt.

6. After months of counting calories, I learned to be (**temperate, lithe**) in eating.

7. Some people criticized the judge as being "too lenient," but I thought she was simply being (**lithe, humane**).

8. In days gone by, a dollar was a(n) (**temperate, appreciable**) sum and was not to be spent lightly.

9. As a public official, I have learned to expect criticism of my ideas, but not (**venomous, temperate**) attacks on my character.

10. After the potatoes have been (**contended, blanched**) in hot water, they should be covered in the olive oil and herb marinade.

11. Isn't it amazing how the Adams family of Massachusetts produced so many (**illustrious, appreciable**) men and women throughout the years?

12. The librarian still (**blanches, contends**) that she was not the only person in the library at midnight, but no one seems to believe her.

Completing the Sentence

Choose the word from the word bank that best completes each of the following sentences. Write the correct word or form of the word in the space provided.

| appreciable | brawny | humane | lithe | venomous |
| blanch | contend | illustrious | temperate | wily |

1. Instead of trying to accomplish something worthwhile on her own, she spends her time boasting about her _____ ancestors.

2. Only when the new drug was administered did the patient begin to show _____ signs of improvement.

3. The years had _____ the auburn from his hair, which now resembled a crown of snowy white.

4. We learned too late that the _____ fox had escaped our trap by doubling back on its own tracks.

5. While a weight lifter generally has a muscular build, a gymnast typically is slim and _____.

6. Despite her image as a "hard-boiled businesswoman," she is notably _____ in her dealings with all of her employees.

7. The _____ scout leader hoisted the canoe on his shoulders and carried it up the steep hill.

8. The mountain climbers had to _____ with unfavorable weather and with the fatigue brought on by high altitude.

9. The bite of the rattlesnake and the sarcastic words of a supposed friend can be equally _____.

10. Mexico City is located deep in the tropics, but because of the altitude, its climate is _____.

Synonyms

Choose the word or form of the word from this Unit that is the same or most nearly the same in meaning as the **boldface** word or expression in the phrase. Write that word on the line. Use a dictionary if necessary.

1. prosecuted by the authorities for **sacrilege** _____
2. a **supple** and graceful beech tree _____
3. **battle** with the opposition _____
4. a **joint** effort to find a solution _____
5. the **husky** arms of the village blacksmith _____
6. the **perceptible** increase in temperature _____
7. a comedian's **flippant** humor _____
8. **mistreated** by the ruling class _____
9. a **clever** and manipulative person _____
10. has a **mellow** attitude _____
11. a toothache that is **unendurable** _____
12. exiled for **treasonous** acts _____
13. born into a **prominent** family _____
14. take time to **think over** the offer _____
15. **go pale** at the sight of blood _____

Antonyms

Choose the word or form of the word from this Unit that is most nearly opposite in meaning to the **boldface** word or expression in the phrase. Write that word on the line. Use a dictionary if necessary.

1. a **dictatorial** regime _____
2. made from **natural** materials _____
3. the **easy** assignment _____
4. **cruel** treatment of animals _____
5. **benevolent** comments _____

Writing: Words in Action

Write a brief letter to one of the speakers in the passage (pages 168–169), Monique or Rafael, explaining whether you agree or disagree with his or her position. Add an example or anecdote of your own to support your views on social networking. Use at least two details from the passage and three or more words from this Unit.

Vocabulary in Context

*Some of the words you have studied in this Unit appear in **boldface** type. Read the passage below, and then circle the letter of the correct answer for each word as it is used in context.*

The cell phone is not just for talking anymore. In 2010, 82 percent of adults in the United States used cell phones, and increasing mobile usage in recent years has led to a **concerted** plan to improve mobile technology. With the advent of the smartphone, cell phones are now devices for messaging other mobile users, accessing social media, and connecting to the Internet. Although the first mobile software applications, more commonly known as "apps," were created in 2008, 1.9 million apps were available for download by 2015. This **appreciable** increase has been a result of **wily** app developers capitalizing on a market that is always poised for innovation.

In 2015, social media, music streaming, and entertainment apps were among the most widely used by smartphone owners. Yet apps vary widely—many make life simpler by helping users complete daily tasks more efficiently. These apps can make shopping lists, manage family schedules, and provide driving directions. Then there are entertainment apps where the user can play a familiar board game, watch videos, assume the personage of a **brawny** wrestler, or let their **lithe** fingers dance across simulated piano keys. An app exists for almost anything that a user can imagine.

Some experts contend that smartphone technology and apps have not made life simpler. Before mobile devices, it was considered a kind of **blasphemy** to be on a phone during family meals. Nowadays, though, that is a common sight. Time will tell whether apps will help users communicate more effectively with one another or lead people to lead separate, insular lives.

---

1. A **concerted** plan is

  a. useless   **c.** weak

  b. energetic   **d.** cooperative

2. An **appreciable** increase is

  a. easy to admire   **c.** sufficient to be noticed

  b. suitable for debate   **d.** difficult to recognize

3. App developers are **wily** because they are

  a. cautious   **c.** independent

  b. shrewd   **d.** foolish

4. Someone who is **brawny** is

  a. strong   **c.** wise

  b. friendly   **d.** mature

5. **Lithe** fingers are

  a. slender   **c.** limber

  b. sturdy   **d.** smooth

6. The word **blasphemy** most nearly means

  a. agreement   **c.** collaboration

  b. irreverence   **d.** decisiveness

Vocabulary for Comprehension
Part 1

*Read this passage, which contains words in **boldface** that appear in Units 10–12. Then choose the best answer to each question based on what is stated or implied in the passage. You may refer to the passage as often as necessary.*

Questions 1–10 are based on the following passage.

Since 1991, when the state of Minnesota passed the first enabling legislation, the charter school movement in the United States has grown rapidly.
(5) There are now about 7,000 charter schools in more than forty states, with an enrollment of approximately three million students. In some cities, charter schools comprise the majority at the elementary
(10) and secondary levels. Such schools are highly controversial, inspiring both fervent support and **skeptical** criticism from parents, teachers, and education experts.

While all charter schools **aspire** to
(15) increase educational quality, a fair evaluation of their progress must emphasize the diversity in their governance and structure. Charter school legislation differs state by state. Each school
(20) negotiates its own contract, or charter. Schools may be the result of a **concerted** effort by teachers, parents, activists, or a combination of all three groups. Charter schools are generally less subject to rules,
(25) regulations, and state and community **statutes**. Each school has policies and agreements governing its curriculum and admissions, assessment, disciplinary, and accountability procedures. At the start of
(30) the movement, the **proponents** of charter schools envisioned that they would operate more like businesses than traditional public schools. Indeed, some charters now operate for profit, and corporations are
(35) sometimes permitted by school districts to manage multiple charter schools. This feature has entailed controversial—some

would say **intolerable**—grants of public money to private corporations.
(40) It is important to recognize that its early stages coincided historically with the No Child Left Behind (NCLB) Act of 2002. NCLB, federal legislation intended to "close the achievement gap," mandated
(45) assessment of all students in grades 3 through 8 in English and mathematics. The tools of choice for this assessment were standardized tests. Depending on each state's criteria, a school's failure to
(50) meet annual standards incurred penalties.

The intersection of NCLB with the **appreciable** growth of charters had some interesting results. Originally intended to supplement and cooperate with public
(55) schools, charters soon became their competition. Moreover, the deregulation of charters gave them certain advantages in some areas. Charter schools, for example, could shape their admissions policies to
(60) exclude underachieving students, thus effortlessly boosting the average grades. They could cap class sizes and limit total school enrollment. In some states, teachers at charter schools did not need
(65) state certification. Some charter schools could outspend their public school counterparts, since they received additional support from the private sector.

But perhaps most important for the
(70) students themselves, the freedom of charter schools to shape their own curriculum meant that, at least in some schools, preparing for tests took the seat at the head of the class. **Adept**
(75) preparation for assessments in English and math crowded out most other

subjects. If the school's test scores were good, as happened at many charters, faculty and managers were happy. But
(80) higher numbers, many critics **contend**, came at the price of a skewed curriculum too focused on assessments.

1. The primary purpose of the passage is
  A) to show that the charter school movement hasn't realized its ideals.
  B) to emphasize the similarities of charter and public schools.
  C) to argue that charter schools should not be run for profit.
  D) to give an overview of the history and intent of charter schools.

2. According lines 14–39, the mosaic of charter schools does not include
  A) sports academies.
  B) schools founded by parents and teachers.
  C) schools managed by corporations.
  D) schools that negotiate their own individual contracts with the state.

3. As it is used in line 21, "concerted" most nearly means
  A) diffused.
  B) cooperative.
  C) unilateral.
  D) registered.

4. As it is used in line 38, "intolerable" most nearly means
  A) outrageous.
  B) incomprehensible.
  C) materialistic.
  D) amiable.

5. What is the author's point in lines 40–50?
  A) Charter schools would not have existed if there had been no NCLB Act.
  B) The NCLB legislation called charter schools' existence into question.
  C) The NCLB Act encouraged the use of standardized tests in charter schools.
  D) The achievement gap persisted despite the goals of the NCLB Act.

6. Which choice provides the best evidence for the answer in the previous question?
  A) Lines 40–42 ("It is . . . 2002")
  B) Lines 43–46 ("NCLB . . . mathematics")
  C) Lines 47–48 ("The tools . . . tests")
  D) Lines 48–50 ("Depending . . . penalties")

7. It can reasonably be inferred from the argument in lines 53–68 that many critics of charter schools have focused on
  A) the inadequacies of standardized tests.
  B) the schools' failure to abide by the provisions of NCLB.
  C) the advantages that deregulation has given charters over public schools.
  D) the ways in which charter schools have dealt with underachieving students.

8. In lines 58–63, the author implies that the ability of charters to cap class size and limit school enrollment
  A) was a loophole not foreseen by the founders of the charter movement.
  B) has often resulted in a better school performance record.
  C) was an result of insufficient funding.
  D) made no difference to students' performance in English and math.

9. As it is used in line 74, "adept" most nearly means
  A) inept.
  B) skilled.
  C) incessant.
  D) restless.

10. The author describes test preparation as taking the "seat at the head of the class" to
  A) emphasize that charter schools made high test scores a priority.
  B) show that test scores have remained constant over the past five years.
  C) explain that charter schools have their own standardized testing requirements.
  D) prove that the standardized tests used at charter schools are more challenging than those used at public schools.

Vocabulary for Comprehension

Part 2

*Read these passages, which contain words in **boldface** that appear in Units 10–12. Then choose the best answer to each question based on what is stated or implied in the passage(s). You may refer to the passages as often as necessary.*

Questions 1–10 are based on the following passages.

Passage 1

Unless they are **garbled** by bias or emotional incoherence, eyewitness narratives usually produce vivid, lasting impressions on their audience. When
(5) serving as U.S. Minister to France, for example, Thomas Jefferson **rendered** his firsthand impressions of the outbreak of the French Revolution in a letter to John Jay in 1789. Jefferson's account of the
(10) storming of the Bastille—a fourteenth-century fortress used as a prison in Paris—provides a thrilling view of one of history's landmark events. The same can be said for a letter written during the early
(15) days of the Civil War by Union Major Sullivan Ballou to his wife Sarah. In this letter, Ballou expresses confidence that service to his country will maintain the freedoms purchased through war. Ballou's
(20) letter allows us, more than 150 years later, to evaluate the motives that guided many of those who took up arms in the conflict.

In a different medium, Herbert Morrison's live radio broadcast captured
(25) the unexpected horror of the *Hindenburg* disaster in New Jersey in May 1937. The *Hindenburg* was a giant passenger airship. Just before landing, it caught fire and crashed to the ground, killing thirty-
(30) five passengers. As the situation **deteriorated,** Morrison's eyewitness account became steadily more gripping, until the reporter was forced to **recoil** from

the scene. For **relentless** impact, first-
(35) person accounts are highly effective.

Passage 2

Human books? That's the metaphor behind an initiative called the Human Library. Started in 2000 in Denmark, the Human Library has spread worldwide.
(40) The program's goal was to curb youth violence, but now its aims are to reduce prejudice, increase **humane** understanding and social justice, and promote **extemporaneous** dialogue
(45) between people who might normally never meet each other.

The concept is simple: Instead of checking out a book from a conventional library, you check out a person for a
(50) conversation that lasts, on average, thirty minutes. The people available, all of whom are volunteers, are listed in the library's "catalogue," and they might range from a refugee to a returning veteran to a brain
(55) tumor survivor. What most of them have in common is that they have, to some degree or other, an interesting life history to **divulge.** Rather than borrowing a book, you "borrow" a person who has unique
(60) stories to share.

The premise of the Human Library is that direct contact with such individuals, and exposure to their first-person point of view in conversation, can make us all
(65) more **enlightened** members of society. The first such program in the United States unfolded at the public library in

Santa Monica, CA, in 2009. Since then, the Human Library has spread to
(70) Rochester, NY; Chicago, IL; and Williams College in western Massachusetts. Challenging prejudice through social contact is an idea whose time is now.

1. What does the author of Passage 1 consider to be the primary value of the letters described?
A) They form the basis of modern-day memoirs of politicians.
B) They are similar to autobiographies written by celebrities.
C) They are valuable accounts by eyewitnesses of historic events.
D) They provide important military strategies.

2. As it is used in line 1, "garbled" most nearly means
A) transformed.
B) jumbled.
C) articulated.
D) rationalized.

3. As it is used in line 33, "recoil" most nearly means
A) shrink back.
B) advance.
C) try again.
D) stiffen.

4. As it is used in line 44, "extemporaneous" most nearly means
A) immediate.
B) protracted.
C) topical.
D) spontaneous.

5. In Passage 2, the "catalogue" of the Human Library consists of
A) people with a story to tell.
B) volunteers with time to tell stories.
C) written interviews with interesting people.
D) journal entries of veterans and survivors.

6. Which statement best describes the overall relationship between Passage 1 and Passage 2?
A) Passage 1 stresses the impact of first-person accounts, while Passage 2 focuses on justice and understanding.
B) Passage 1 is more concerned with nonfiction examples than Passage 2 is.
C) Passage 2 cites more historical figures and events than Passage 1 does.
D) Passage 1 shows many viewpoints, but Passage 2 uses first-person narration.

7. As it is used in line 58, "divulge" most nearly means
A) reveal.
B) conceal.
C) reconstruct.
D) support.

8. The author of Passage 1 would most likely regard the premise of the Human Library, as it is identified in lines 36–46 of Passage 2,
A) as unrealistic, given the inequalities of contemporary society.
B) as impractical, given the considerable cost of Human Library programs.
C) with approval because of the impressions generated by first-person point of view.
D) with skepticism because letters are a more effective way of communication than face-to-face encounters.

9. In Passage 1, the author emphasizes the impact of eyewitnesses' letters and a radio broadcast. In Passage 2, the author focuses on the importance of
A) library research.
B) extemporaneous dialogue.
C) unique first-person stories
D) growth of Human Library programs.

10. Which choice provides the best evidence for the answer to the previous question?
A) Lines 38–39 ("Started . . . worldwide")
B) Lines 51–53 ("people . . . 'catalogue'")
C) Lines 58–60 ("Rather . . . share")
D) Lines 72–73 ("Challenging . . . now")

Synonyms

*From the word bank below, choose the word that has the same or nearly the same meaning as the **boldface** word in each sentence and write it on the line. You will not use all of the words.*

aspire	deteriorate	invincible	preamble
blanch	extemporaneous	irreverent	reek
comport	garble	mire	rivulet
despicable	illustrious	obtrusive	skeptical

1. His behavior is not usually so **brash**, but he was so nervous and eager to talk to his favorite writer that he forgot his manners. _____

2. The actress has been known to **conduct** herself with dignity even when faced with outrageous questions from reporters _____

3. The show's producers did not expect their **spontaneous** remarks or they would have scheduled more time for the program. _____

4. A good journalist will not **misrepresent** these events but will report them accurately and factually. _____

5. So many **renowned** figures have graduated from the university that you cannot deny it will be a great place to make connections. _____

6. His ability to strike out the best hitters in the league has given him a reputation as an **unbeatable** pitcher. _____

7. No one could locate the source of the **stench** in the house until someone found the bag of garbage left behind by the previous owner. _____

8. My drawing skills always **worsen** over the summer when I am not taking the weekly art classes at school. _____

9. I am usually a forgiving person, but my former friend's actions are so **detestable** that I don't wish to ever speak to her again. _____

10. I received an **incredulous** look when I announced my goal of writing a novel because they did not think I would follow through. _____

11. The comedian lost numerous fans after making **disrespectful** comments. _____

12. The **opening** of the book states that none of the characters or situations are based on real people or events. _____

Two-Word Completions

Select the pair of words that best completes the meaning of each of the following sentences.

1. The _____ statistics cited in the magazine article certainly _____ its effectiveness. If the author had made sure that his figures were correct, his argument might have been more convincing.
   a. laborious . . . enlightened
   b. bleak . . . quavered
   c. erroneous . . . impaired
   d. slipshod . . . rendered

2. She has always been a strong _____ of organic, natural ingredients in foods, so I wonder why she tolerates the _____ sweeteners and food colorings in diet sodas.
   a. proponent . . . synthetic
   b. adept . . . languid
   c. statute . . . subversive
   d. temperate . . . venomous

3. A ballerina's _____ and graceful figure contrasts sharply with a weight lifter's massively _____ physique.
   a. slipshod . . . rugged
   b. diminutive . . . concise
   c. lithe . . . brawny
   d. demure . . . languid

4. I did everything I could to _____ his cunning attempts to undermine my authority in the company; unfortunately, he proved too _____ and persistent for me to anticipate all his moves all the time.
   a. forestall . . . wily
   b. divulge . . . slipshod
   c. subvert . . . demure
   d. chide . . . impair

5. When Shakespeare's Polonius says that _____ is the soul of wit, he extols the virtues of a _____ and succinct phrase.
   a. blasphemy . . . wily
   b. brevity . . . concise
   c. brawn . . . venomous
   d. depreciation . . . staccato

6. Her talents are just average, but she has _____ them to the fullest. On the other hand, he was given great natural abilities, but he has _____ them on trifles.
   a. divulged . . . recouped
   b. contended . . . forestalled
   c. exploited . . . squandered
   d. pondered . . . impaired

7. Though a(n) _____ master might deal kindly and generously with his or her animals, a cruel one would _____ and abuse them.
   a. relentless . . . exploit
   b. humane . . . maltreat
   c. enlightened . . . emancipate
   d. autocratic . . . impair

Denotation and Connotation

The dictionary definition of a word is its **denotation**. The denotation is what the word actually means. A word's denotation has a literal, *neutral* meaning, without positive or negative implied meanings.

Words that have similar denotations can have different **connotations**—suggested, or implied, meanings that readers or listeners associate with the word. For example, the word *tense* has a relatively neutral connotation, while the words *anxious* and *apprehensive*, which share a similar denotation, have a more negative connotation.

Consider these synonyms for the neutral word *spend*:

purchase   acquire   splurge   squander

Purchase and *acquire* have neutral or mildly positive connotations, while *splurge* and *squander* have negative connotations.

Look at these examples of words that are similar in denotation but have different connotations.

NEUTRAL	POSITIVE	NEGATIVE
brevity	succinctness	terseness
quiet	temperate	diffident
smell	scent	reek

Expressing the Connotation

Read each sentence. Select the word in parentheses that expresses the connotation (positive, negative, or neutral) given at the beginning of the sentence.

neutral
1. The black kitten, (**diminutive, small**) but lively and alert, quickly won my heart.

negative
2. The editorial offended some readers, who found the tone too (**lighthearted, irreverent**) for such a serious subject.

negative
3. The salesperson explained the rules of the sweepstakes in a (**slipshod, concise**) manner.

neutral
4. If you are in a hurry to get going, Andrew's (**unhurried, languid**) manner can be frustrating.

positive
5. I tried to (**hinder, forestall**) any ideas he had about inviting me to the school dance on Friday by mentioning my intention to stay at home.

positive
6. Our (**hardworking, relentless**) boss made us stay late to finish the project.

negative
7. Since he seldom gave me a direct answer, I was (**skeptical, unsure**) of his intentions.

positive
8. The chairperson's speeches were often witty, engaging, and insightful, in spite of the fact that they were (**unplanned, extemporaneous**).

Classical Roots

spec, spic—to look

This root appears in **despicable** (page 146), which means "that which is to be looked down at." Some other words based on this root are listed below.

aspect	introspection	prospective	respective
conspicuous	perspicacious	retrospect	specter

From the list of words above, choose the one that corresponds to each of the brief definitions below. Write the word in the blank space in the illustrative sentence below the definition. Use an online or print dictionary if necessary.

1. a phantom, apparition; a fearful image or threatening possibility

The hooded figure was a frightening _____ that Halloween night.

2. noticeable, drawing attention

We never expected to enjoy living in such a large and _____ building.

3. an examination of one's own thoughts and feelings (*"looking within"*)

The recluse was given to long hours of _____ and meditation.

4. keen in observing and understanding (*"able to see through"*)

Nineteenth-century writer Alexis de Tocqueville was a(n) _____ observer of American society, politics, and culture of the day.

5. an appearance; a side or view; the direction something faces

It's important to consider all _____ of an issue before coming to a conclusion.

6. with reference to the past; a survey of the past (*"a looking back"*)

"In _____," he mused, "my college years were probably some of the happiest times of my life, though I certainly didn't realize it at the time."

7. belonging to each; individual (*"looking back and forth"*)

Mother sent the children to their _____ rooms to cool off after the argument.

8. looked forward to, expected

I plan to invite my _____ sister-in-law out to lunch next week.

*Read the following passage, taking note of the **boldface** words and their contexts. These words are among those you will be studying in Unit 13. It may help you to complete the exercises in this Unit if you refer to the way the words are used below.*

From Trash to Tabletop
<Interview>

Interviewer: Sherlynia Singh, as the owner of Frank's Fish Shop on Washington Avenue, what do you think is the most interesting development in your business today?

Singh: My father, who was a fisherman, used to say, "Give a man a fish, and you feed him for a day. Teach a man to fish, and you feed him for a lifetime." I think it's ironic that overfishing, the depleting of our fish stocks, is now a great challenge to us all. The oceans cannot produce fish **ad infinitum**. I have become fascinated by the rising interest in trash fish, which might help us to solve this problem.

Interviewer: What are trash fish?

Singh: Trash fish are fish that consumers don't like—they're not popular food sources, and they don't fetch high prices in the marketplace. Most commercial fishing operations target high-value fish, like tuna, salmon, or cod. Such operations use huge nets or long lines with hundreds of hooks to catch thousands of fish at a time. In the process, they pick up a lot of so-called trash fish. Once, these low-value fish were discarded, but now they are retained and processed for sale.

Interviewer: What changed people's minds about fish once considered trash?

Singh: Most experts would **concede** that the growth of fish-farming is a major factor. Since overfishing has caused wild populations of popular species to **wane**, more of the fish we eat comes from fish farms. Many fish farms raise high-value carnivorous species, like salmon and tuna, that require massive quantities of food. Increasingly, it's trash fish that are processed to make fish meal and fish oils used to feed farmed fish. Since fish-farming relies on wild-caught trash fish, overfishing our oceans is still a problem. But without trash fish, fish-farming would soon become **untenable**.

Interviewer: So, trash fish play an important role in fish-farming, but they aren't consumed by humans.

Singh: Actually, some trash fish does find its way to our dinner table. Small, family-run fishing enterprises are still common in developing countries, often operating in rather **sordid** conditions. Local fishermen **apportion** some of their catch—the low-value fish—for home consumption and sell the rest of their yield to others. In many countries, great quantities of fish we consider low-value are sold for human consumption. This is often a matter of local preferences. In much of East Asia, for example, a wide variety of low- and high-value fish are an important part of the traditional diet.

These fish are the by-product of commercial shrimp-fishing.

Saltwater salmon pens on a fish farm in the United States

Interviewer: It sounds as if determining whether or not a fish species is a trash fish might be a matter of opinion.

Singh: To some extent, that's true, but our taste for fish has changed as supplies have changed. When popular species become less common due to overfishing, environmental changes, or **migration**, local fisheries find new species to satisfy demand. Tuna is a classic example. In the days before refrigeration and canning, tuna flesh would quickly become **rancid**, so tuna was unpopular and usually discarded. That changed early in the twentieth century, when a sudden drop in sardine populations prompted fisheries to start catching tuna off the California coast. Before long, tuna had become one of the most popular and **versatile** fish consumed in America, and it's now one of the most highly valued fish in the world. A single bluefin tuna can fetch $150,000 in a Tokyo market today! That's quite a **lofty** sum.

Interviewer: So, sellers and buyers alike are learning that yesterday's trash fish can become tomorrow's food fish.

Singh: It sounds **perverse**, but it's true. The fishing industry is rapidly changing due to environmental problems, over-fishing, and innovations in fish-farming. People forget that many fish that are popular around the world today were **perceived** as "trash" not long ago: hake, tilapia, Chilean sea bass, pangasius, monkfish, and shark all fall into this category. For years, I predicted we would expand our seafood diet to include more overlooked species, and now that people have done so, I feel **vindicated**. It seems that, for many species, status as a trash fish is only a **prelude** to **bona fide** popularity.

Audio

For iWords and audio passages, go to SadlierConnect.com.

Definitions

Note the spelling, pronunciation, part(s) of speech, and definition(s) of each of the following words. Then write the appropriate form of the word in the blank space in the illustrative sentence(s) following.

1. **apportion**
(ə pôr′ shən)

(*v.*) to divide and give out in shares
The aging king decided to _____ the lands of his vast kingdom among his three daughters.

2. **buoyant**
(boi′ ənt)

(*adj.*) able to float easily; able to hold things up; cheerful, hopeful
We were weary and anxious to get home, but our friend's _____ spirits kept us going.

3. **clique**
(klēk; klik)

(*n.*) a small, exclusive group of people
The queen was surrounded by a _____ of powerful nobles who actually ran the country.

4. **congenial**
(kən jēn′ yəl)

(*adj.*) getting on well with others; agreeable, pleasant
I was relieved when my bunkmate at summer camp turned out to be considerate and _____.

5. **migration**
(mī grā′ shən)

(*n.*) a movement from one country or region to another
_____ from north to south has contributed to the political clout of the Sun Belt.

6. **perverse**
(pər vərs′)

(*adj.*) inclined to go against what is expected; stubborn; turned away from what is good and proper
Some teenagers get _____ pleasure from blasting music that their parents do not like.

7. **rancid**
(ran′ sid)

(*adj.*) stale, spoiled
When he opened the door, there poured forth the unmistakably _____ odor of some ancient leftovers.

8. **sever**
(sev′ ər)

(*v.*) to separate, divide into parts
It was extreme of her to _____ ties with her former best friend, but that is what she did.

9. **untenable**
(ən ten′ ə bəl)

(*adj.*) not capable of being held or defended; impossible to maintain

Minutes into the debate she had a sinking feeling that her position was completely _____.

10. **versatile**
(vər′ sə təl)

(*adj.*) able to do many things well; capable of many uses

By moving from comedy to drama to musicals, he has shown himself to be a truly _____ actor.

Using Context

*For each item, determine whether the **boldface** word from pages 190–191 makes sense in the context of the sentence. Circle the item numbers next to the six sentences in which the words are used correctly.*

1. Wood is a **versatile** material that can be used to make everything from chopsticks to houses.

2. Because that horse has a stubborn and **perverse** nature, only an expert rider should take him out on the trail or into the ring.

3. Refrigeration keeps lettuce, spinach, and other leafy vegetables crisp and **rancid**.

4. If the crab's legs were to **sever** during an attack by a predator, they would likely regenerate, or grow back.

5. A life jacket will keep a person **buoyant**, even if he or she does not know how to swim.

6. Inside the cave, hundreds of bats gathered together in a **clique**, each one hanging upside-down from the ceiling and sleeping until dusk.

7. The workers bolted the new section into place, making a strong and **congenial** joint.

8. Without any evidence to support your hypothesis, it is completely **untenable**.

9. When we **apportion** the workload among ourselves, let's make sure we do so evenly.

10. Scientists are concerned about the **migration** of that bird species and fear that the birds might become extinct if their numbers keep dropping.

Choosing the Right Word

*Select the **boldface** word that better completes each sentence. You might refer to the passage on pages 188–189 to see how most of these words are used in context. Note that the choices might be related forms of the Unit words.*

1. Leonardo da Vinci was a (**versatile, buoyant**) genius who excelled in many different fields of art and science.

2. Our team was more than just (**untenable, congenial**); our friendships were meaningful and deep, and we were very involved in one another's lives.

3. Our problem now is not to (**sever, apportion**) blame for our failures, but to find a way to achieve success.

4. A good politician must appear (**perverse, congenial**) even when he or she is feeling cross and unsociable.

5. The psychologist said that troubled young people often have a (**perverse, rancid**) impulse to do exactly what will be most injurious to them.

6. Because our tank forces had been destroyed, the position of the ground troops proved (**congenial, untenable**).

7. You are at a stage of life when you should begin to (**apportion, sever**) the apron strings that tie you to your mother.

8. American society has been deeply affected by the steady (**migration, clique**) from the inner city to the suburbs.

9. This (**versatile, untenable**) new kitchen tool can chop, slice, and blend. I wish it could do the cooking, too!

10. The atmosphere in the tiny, airless cell soon grew as (**buoyant, rancid**) as the foul-smelling soup that the prisoner was fed every night.

11. There are more than 100 members in the state legislature, but the real power is held by a small (**clique, migration**) of insiders.

12. I could tell from her animated expression and her sprightly step that she was in a (**buoyant, versatile**) mood.

Completing the Sentence

Choose the word from the word bank that best completes each of the following sentences. Write the correct word or form of the word in the space provided.

apportion	clique	migration	rancid	untenable
buoyant	congenial	perverse	sever	versatile

1. He's not really hungry; he's just being _____ in insisting on eating now.

2. We found it easy to float in the lake because the high salt content makes the water extremely _____.

3. It takes a really _____ athlete to win varsity letters in three different sports.

4. The seasonal _____ of birds southward reminds us that we have come to the end of the summer vacation.

5. Although many of my friends seem to like her, I've never found her to be a particularly _____ companion.

6. The oil, which had been inadvertently stored in a heated room, soon began to exude a rank odor that told us it had turned _____.

7. I am convinced that the drama club is run by a(n) _____ of students who reserve all the best roles for themselves.

8. Since the theory is based on inaccurate and out-of-date information, it is clearly _____.

9. New employees are assigned their duties by the office manager, who is responsible for _____ work among the staff.

10. In 1776 the Continental Congress moved to _____ all political connections between the colonies and Great Britain.

Definitions

Note the spelling, pronunciation, part(s) of speech, and definition(s) of each of the following words. Then write the appropriate form of the word in the blank space in the illustrative sentence(s) following.

1. ad infinitum
(ad in fə nī' təm)

(*adv.*) endlessly
Children who hear a favorite story read over and over
_____ are learning about language.

2. bona fide
(bō' nə fīd)

(*adj.*) genuine; sincere
The appraiser studied the old book and declared it to be
a _____ first edition of *Moby-Dick*.

3. concede
(kən sēd')

(*v.*) to admit as true; to yield, submit
Even though the votes were all in and counted, the losing
candidate refused to _____ the election.

4. lofty
(lôf' tē)

(*adj.*) very high; noble
My mentor maintains _____ standards
and works hard to adhere to them.

5. perceive
(pər sēv')

(*v.*) to be aware of through the senses, observe; to grasp
mentally
I thought I _____ a flicker of guilt on
my brother's face when I asked who ate my slice of pie.

6. prelude
(pre' lüd)

(*n.*) an introduction; that which comes before or leads off
The orchestral _____ to the new opera
seemed more interesting to me than the opera itself.

7. rustic
(rəs' tik)

(*adj.*) country-like; simple, plain; awkward; (*n.*) one who
lives in the country
We rented a _____ cabin, with no
electricity or running water, twenty miles from the town.
On the trail we met an amiable old _____
carrying a fishing pole and a string of trout he'd caught.

8. sordid
(sôr' did)

(*adj.*) wretchedly poor; run-down; mean or selfish
Nineteenth-century reformers made people aware of just
how _____ conditions were in city slums.

9. **vindicate**
(vin′ də kāt)

(v.) to clear from hint or charge of wrongdoing; to defend successfully against opposition; to justify

Though the accused was _____ in the end, his career was all but ruined by the allegations.

10. **wane**
(wān)

(v.) to lose size, strength, or power

As the moon _____, the nights grew darker; we could hardly see our way along the forest trails.

Using Context

*For each item, determine whether the **boldface** word from pages 194–195 makes sense in the context of the sentence. Circle the item numbers next to the six sentences in which the words are used correctly.*

1. The soccer team was determined to **vindicate** the opposing team, who had won the previous year's final match.

2. The dance recital began with an entertaining **prelude** that showcased the talents of some of the dancers who would appear in the show.

3. The **sordid** details provided in the biography helped me to understand why the movie director had been inspired to work in the film industry.

4. The bags, said to be **bona fide** designer purses, turned out to be well-manufactured fakes.

5. After I lost the board game to my friend a third time, I had to **concede** that he was a better player.

6. The green, **lofty** field was filled with wildflowers and grazing deer.

7. That popular song is stuck in my head after being played **ad infinitum** on the radio.

8. The **rustic** décor of the house looked even more elegant and modern when compared with the dense woods outside.

9. My attention often starts to **wane** after hours of studying, signaling that I need to give my mind a break.

10. I **perceive** a flinch of annoyance on your face about the lateness of this meeting.

Choosing the Right Word

*Select the **boldface** word that better completes each sentence. You might refer to the passage on pages 188–189 to see how most of these words are used in context. Note that the choices might be related forms of the Unit words.*

1. The long range of (**sordid, lofty**) mountains was dramatically silhouetted against the glowing purple, red, and pink sunset.

2. They will not be allowed to vote in the election because they are not considered (**ad infinitum, bona fide**) residents of the community.

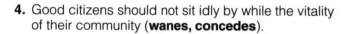

3. When she came home from college for Thanksgiving break, she treated us "high school kids" with (**sordid, lofty**) scorn.

4. Good citizens should not sit idly by while the vitality of their community (**wanes, concedes**).

5. I appreciate her interest in me, but I am annoyed by her tendency to offer criticism and advice (**bona fide, ad infinitum**).

6. The general's army was in full retreat, and he was forced to (**vindicate, concede**) that his nation had lost the war.

7. Shakespeare's clowns are often simple (**preludes, rustics**) who are trying to behave like sophisticated men of the world.

8. One of the aims of education is to enable us to (**perceive, wane**) the difference between what is truly excellent and what is second-rate.

9. They claimed to be unselfish patriots, but we knew that, in reality, they were acting from the most (**rustic, sordid**) motives.

10. My faith in that seemingly ordinary young girl was entirely (**vindicated, perceived**).

11. The successful invasion of France in June 1944 was only a (**prelude, rustic**) to the great Allied victories that ended the war in Europe.

12. He talks a great game of tennis, but I (**wane, concede**) nothing to him until he has shown that he can beat me on the court.

Completing the Sentence

Choose the word from the word bank that best completes each of the following sentences. Write the correct word or form of the word in the space provided.

ad infinitum	concede	perceive	rustic	vindicate
bona fide	lofty	prelude	sordid	wane

1. When the mayor failed to carry out her campaign promises, her popularity quickly _____, and she failed to win reelection.

2. I realize that I made a bad mistake, but at least I possess the strength of character to _____ that I was wrong and apologize.

3. The early cold spell proved to be a fitting _____ to one of the most severe winters of modern times.

4. Who would believe that this peaceful, _____ hideaway is only twenty-five miles from the city?

5. Dismissing all his rivals as impostors, the undefeated heavyweight boxer pronounced himself the only _____ contender for the crown.

6. The accused clerk _____ herself by producing signed receipts for all the questioned items.

7. It is a regrettable fact of our history that several presidential administrations have been tainted by _____ scandals.

8. Isn't it boring when people go on and on about their looks, their clothes, and their popularity _____?

9. The Declaration of Independence first set forth the _____ standards to which we as a nation have ever since aspired.

10. We began to _____ the impact of the tornado only after viewing the flattened neighborhood and interviewing residents.

Synonyms

*Choose the word or form of the word from this Unit that is the same or most nearly the same in meaning as the **boldface** word or expression in the phrase. Write that word on the line. Use a dictionary if necessary.*

1. a move to **break off** relations with that country _____
2. a **coterie** of influential donors _____
3. a **mass movement** to the suburbs _____
4. watched the initial enthusiasm **dwindle** _____
5. a charming **rural** scene _____
6. shocked by their **wayward** behavior _____
7. **cleared** of the charges _____
8. ridiculously **groundless** reasons _____
9. her elevated mood and **blithe** spirit _____
10. a **handy** gadget with many uses _____
11. a kind and **friendly** host _____
12. **parcel out** land to the farmers _____
13. the **lead-in** to a successful event _____
14. the odor of **sour** milk _____
15. the **towering** mountain peaks _____

Antonyms

*Choose the word or form of the word from this Unit that is most nearly opposite in meaning to the **boldface** word or expression in the phrase. Write that word on the line. Use a dictionary if necessary.*

1. listened **briefly** to his favorite song _____
2. **be blind to** a problem _____
3. a **counterfeit** copy _____
4. **deny** defeat in battle _____
5. given shelter in a **spotless** room _____

Writing: Words in Action

Why are certain fish formerly considered "trash" now being considered suitable for people to eat? Write an essay describing this transition. Cite specific examples from your observations, studies, reading (refer to pages 188–189), or personal experience. Use three or more words from this Unit.

Vocabulary in Context

*Some of the words you have studied in this Unit appear in **boldface** type. Read the passage below, and then circle the letter of the correct answer for each word as it is used in context.*

The Alaskan pollock was once considered a trash fish. Few consumers wanted to eat pollock, a big-eyed groundfish native to the icy waters of the Bering Sea, so the fish attracted little interest from commercial fishermen. But a trash fish today can become a **bona fide** gold mine tomorrow. The rise of fast food and cheap sushi helped **sever** the pollock from its humble history. Breaded and battered pollock fillets proved to be tasty fish sticks, now sold by fast-food eateries around the world. And once pollock is processed into a paste called surimi, it becomes an acceptable imitation of expensive sushi fare, such as crab, shrimp, and lobster. The pollock fishery is now the largest U.S. fishery by volume—over 2 billion tons of pollock are caught each year—and is worth more than $1 billion annually.

Indeed, so much pollock is processed today that the fish may play an unlikely role in the cleanup of a major toxic pollutant. Cities across the nation have massive amounts of lead-contaminated soil—far too much to dig up and haul away. For years, a **clique** of dedicated scientists has been working on the problem. Pollock may provide a solution. Fish bones are full of calcium phosphate, which can neutralize lead by turning it into a harmless mineral. Alaska's pollock plants produce tons of fishbone meal.

Giant sacks of fishbone meal have been shipped from **rustic** Alaska to South Prescott, a neighborhood of Oakland, California. There, teams of **congenial** workers apply the fishbone to contaminated yards and vacant lots. The treatment creates an odor of dead fish, but the smell dissipates quickly, and local residents are **buoyant** about the project. The smell, they say, is of lead disappearing.

---

1. A **bona fide** gold mine is
   a. metaphorical   **c.** genuine
   b. valuable   **d.** possible

2. The word **sever** most nearly means
   a. deliver   **c.** extend
   b. transform   **d.** separate

3. A **clique** of scientists
   a. is a club   **c.** has popular people
   b. includes enemies   **d.** is an exclusive group

4. A **rustic** area is
   a. country-like   **c.** residential
   b. expensive   **d.** fortunate

5. Workers who are **congenial** are
   a. professional   **c.** highly trained
   b. pleasant   **d.** college educated

6. To be **buoyant** is to be
   a. informed   **c.** hesitant
   b. hopeful   **d.** trustful

*Read the following passage, taking note of the **boldface** words and their contexts. These words are among those you will be studying in Unit 14. It may help you to complete the exercises in this Unit if you refer to the way the words are used below.*

Seven Wonders
<Magazine Article>

The conquests of Alexander the Great broadened the horizons of the ancient Greek world. Many territories **annexed** by Alexander were home to civilizations with longer **pedigrees** than the Greeks', such as Babylon and Egypt. Each of these civilizations had its own culture, its own style of architecture, art, music, and cuisine. Each had its own traditions and history. Commerce and curiosity **incited** interest in travel. A steady **influx** of travelers was drawn to major cities and famous landmarks. Moved by the **profuse** interest in travel, Greek authors compiled lists of spectacular sites. **Cleaving** to custom, these ancient travel writers normally included seven locations in their lists. In ancient times, the sites listed varied from one author to another. But today the landmarks mentioned in these ancient travel guides are remembered as the Seven Wonders of the World.

Statues of the Gods

The Statue of Zeus soared more than 40 feet high. Built in 432 BCE, it sat in a temple in Olympia, on mainland Greece. Across the

Aegean, on the island of Rhodes, a bronze statue of the sun god Helios guarded the harbor from atop a massive stone pillar, which served as its **cornerstone**. The giant statue of Helios was known as the Colossus of Rhodes.

Temple and Tomb

The Temple of Artemis was located in the town of Ephesus on the Anatolian coast, which is in modern-day Turkey. The temple was destroyed and rebuilt twice before the **debacle** of its final destruction at the hands of a rioting mob in 401 CE.

Also on the Anatolian coast was the Tomb of Mausolus, which stood nearly 150 feet high. A provincial governor of the Persian Empire, Mausolus had his capital in Halicarnassus. When he died in 353 BCE, his wife could hardly **reconcile** herself to his death. As a tribute to her husband, she had the great tomb built.

The Lighthouse and the Pyramid

For centuries, the Lighthouse of Alexandria guided Mediterranean navigators into the busy Egyptian port. An engineering marvel that rose to a height of 400 feet above the water, it could be seen 29 miles away by approaching sailors.

The Great Pyramid of Giza is the oldest of the Seven Wonders and the only one that remains standing today. Its endurance is recalled in the old Arabic saying, "Man fears time, but time fears the Pyramids." The builders **improvised** the pyramid's bricks from the local limestone. Its **precipitous** stone walls extended nearly 500 feet in height and reflected the golden **pallor** of the desert sun. Contrary to many accounts, the

Hanging Gardens of Babylon

laborers who built the pyramid were not slaves in **shackles** and **threadbare** clothing, but rather teams of villagers who took pride in their work.

A Garden for a Homesick Queen

The Babylonian king Nebuchadnezzar was extremely active during his long reign. He spent much of his time **embroiled** in wars and engaged in massive building projects. He is credited with constructing the Hanging Gardens of Babylon. According to legend, the king's wife, Amytis of Media, deeply missed her homeland. Media was a land rich in forests and greenery, and Amytis felt **devitalized** in the plains of Babylon. To enliven Amytis's mood, the king ordered the construction of the Hanging Gardens, a lush expanse of trees and plants.

Though nobody can be sure the king's **cordial** gesture had its desired effect, the gardens, like the other wonders, were a marvel of ancient ingenuity, and they attracted sightseers from across the known world.

Great Pyramid of Giza

Audio

For iWords and audio passages, go to SadlierConnect.com.

Definitions

Note the spelling, pronunciation, part(s) of speech, and definition(s) of each of the following words. Then write the appropriate form of the word in the blank space in the illustrative sentence(s) following.

1. annex
(*v.* ə neks';
n. an' eks)

(*v.*) to add to, attach; to incorporate; (*n.*) an attachment or addition
The two nations protested when their militant neighbor _____ the disputed territory.
All back issues of magazines are kept next door on the second floor of the new library _____.

2. cordial
(kôr' jəl)

(*adj.*) in a friendly manner, hearty; cheery; (*n.*) a liqueur
Our aunt's _____ welcome made us all feel right at home in her huge, drafty Victorian house.
Grasshopper pie is made not with grasshoppers but with crème de menthe, a _____.

3. debacle
(di bäk' əl)

(*n.*) an overwhelming defeat, rout; a complete collapse or failure
After the _____ of their crushing loss in the World Series, the team vowed to return next year.

4. embroil
(em broil')

(*v.*) to involve in a conflict or difficulty; to throw into confusion
The last thing I want is to _____ myself in a dispute between two of my best friends.

5. haphazard
(hap haz' ərd)

(*adj.*) by chance, not planned; lacking order
The _____ arrangement of facts in his presentation left his listeners completely confused.

6. improvise
(im' prə vīz))

(*v.*) to compose or perform without preparation; to construct from available materials
After the earthquake, stunned villagers were forced to _____ shelters from the debris.

7. pallor
(pal' ər)

(*n.*) an extreme or unnatural paleness
"A ghost!" the girl gasped, her _____ making her look much like a ghost herself as she ran away.

8. profuse
(prō fyüs')

(*adj.*) very abundant; given or flowing freely
How can I stay upset with him when he is so sincere and _____ with his apologies?

9. reconcile
(rek' ən sīl)

(v.) to restore to friendship; to settle; to resign (oneself)

After so many years of feuding, it will be difficult for the brothers to _____ and begin anew.

10. shackle
(shak' əl)

(v.) to put into chains; (n., usually pl.) a chain, fetter

The guards attempted to _____ the prisoner before allowing him to board the waiting airplane.

His wicked plot discovered, the prince was bound in _____ and taken to the dank dungeon.

Using Context

*For each item, determine whether the **boldface** word from pages 202–203 makes sense in the context of the sentence. Circle the item numbers next to the six sentences in which the words are used correctly.*

1. I hadn't seen her in such a long time that I almost didn't **reconcile** her.

2. Some birds fly in straight paths and orderly formations, but others seem to fly in **haphazard**, zigzag lines.

3. The Wilkinsons' parties are always very enjoyable because they are such **cordial** and considerate hosts.

4. Just as I had hoped, my project was a complete **debacle** and won first place at the science fair.

5. The candidate claims that news outlets are reporting lies about her to **embroil** her in a scandal.

6. Are you the kind of cook who likes to follow a recipe, or do you prefer to **improvise** a meal when you are cooking?

7. The skill and **pallor** that she showed when untying the boat indicated that she was an experienced sailor.

8. Right now, the drip in the faucet is merely **profuse**, but over time it will probably turn into a serious leak.

9. Because of a significant increase in the number of students, the school district is building an **annex** for the middle school.

10. Escape artist Harry Houdini would often **shackle** himself and then submerge himself in water; in order not to drown, he would have to break free.

Choosing the Right Word

*Select the **boldface** word that better completes each sentence. You might refer to the passage on pages 200–201 to see how most of these words are used in context. Note that the choices might be related forms of the Unit words.*

1. The glade was resplendent with (**profuse, haphazard**) flowers.

2. In spite of all the progress made in recent years, we are still not entirely free from the (**shackles, debacles**) of prejudice and superstition.

3. Some people think that, because she wears mismatched clothing, her approach to dressing herself is (**cordial, haphazard**), but I think she plans her outfits very carefully.

4. He is the kind of speaker who is more effective when he (**improvises, embroils**) his remarks than when he reads from a prepared script.

5. How can she (**shackle, reconcile**) her claim that she is a "good citizen" with the fact that she doesn't even bother to vote?

6. The famous actor applied a layer of ashen makeup to simulate the ghastly (**pallor, annex**) of a ghost.

7. The President said in his inaugural address that he firmly believes that we must not (**embroil, reconcile**) ourselves in the quarrels of other nations.

8. My campaign for the class presidency ended in an utter (**pallor, debacle**) when I forgot my speech as I was about to address the assembly.

9. Although I had never even met her, the emails she wrote to me were so (**cordial, profuse**) that I felt we were old friends.

10. The disaster was so great that the overcrowded hospital was forced to house some patients in a makeshift (**annex, debacle**).

11. After he was brought in by the police, he remained (**shackled, embroiled**) to a chair for about half an hour.

12. The couple thanked me so (**profusely, haphazardly**) for the small favor I had done them that I was almost embarrassed.

Completing the Sentence

Choose the word from the word bank that best completes each of the following sentences. Write the correct word or form of the word in the space provided.

annex	debacle	haphazard	pallor	reconcile
cordial	embroil	improvise	profuse	shackle

1. Her deathly _____ and distraught expression told us she had already received the tragic news.

2. With the Louisiana Purchase of 1803, Jefferson _____ a vast territory that doubled the size of the nation.

3. As we grow older and perhaps wiser, we _____ ourselves to the fact that we will never achieve all that we had hoped for in life.

4. Our dress rehearsal was a disaster: Actors blew their lines, and doors on the set got stuck shut; it was a complete _____!

5. Millions of immigrants willingly came to America from all over the world, but many Africans arrived here in _____.

6. The entertainer cleverly _____ limericks and other comic rhymes on subjects suggested by the audience.

7. We certainly did not expect to receive such a(n) _____ greeting from someone who had been described to us as cold and unsociable.

8. Three customers fought noisily over the last sale-priced sweater until they finally _____ the store manager in their dispute.

9. His books are scattered around in such a(n) _____ manner that it is a mystery to me how he can find the ones he wants.

10. In the untended garden the weeds were so _____ that they all but smothered the few flowers that managed to blossom.

Definitions

Note the spelling, pronunciation, part(s) of speech, and definition(s) of each of the following words. Then write the appropriate form of the word in the blank space in the illustrative sentence(s) following.

1. cleave
(klēv)

(*v.*) to cut or split open; to cling to
It is possible to _____ a ripe coconut neatly in two with just one swing of a machete.

2. cornerstone
(kôr′ nər stōn)

(*n.*) the starting point of a building; a fundamental principle or element
The _____ of the American judicial system is the presumption of innocence.

3. devitalize
(dē vīt′ ə līz)

(*v.*) to make weak or lifeless
The long, dark winter, with its cold rain and gloomy skies, _____ her usually buoyant spirit.

4. exonerate
(eg zän′ ə rāt)

(*v.*) to clear from a charge or accusation
The prisoner was set free after ten years, thanks to new evidence that _____ him of all charges.

5. glib
(glib)

(*adj.*) ready and fluent in speech; thoughtless, insincere
The salesman had such _____ answers to every objection that I grew extremely skeptical of his claims.

6. incite
(in sīt′)

(*v.*) to rouse, stir up, urge on
Company agents were hired to _____ a riot at the steelworkers' protest demonstration.

7. influx
(in′ fləks)

(*n.*) a coming in, inflow
An _____ of arctic air has brought unseasonably cold weather to half the country.

8. pedigree
(ped′ ə grē)

(*n.*) a list of ancestors, family tree; the history or origins of something
Despite his impressive _____, the colt showed little enthusiasm for racing.

9. **precipitous**
(pri sip' ət əs)

(*adj.*) very steep
The novice hikers were very nervous as they carefully negotiated the _____ mountain trail.

10. **threadbare**
(thred' bâr)

(*adj.*) shabby, old and worn
My brother has carefully collected a closetful of faded, _____ jeans, sweatshirts, and sneakers.

Using Context

*For each item, determine whether the **boldface** word from pages 206–207 makes sense in the context of the sentence. Circle the item numbers next to the six sentences in which the words are used correctly.*

1. The energy from the audience would always **devitalize** the lead singer and make him even more animated as the show went on.

2. This **threadbare** blanket will hardly keep me warm, but I've held onto it as a memento from my childhood.

3. The **precipitous** weather forecast suggests that we will not be able to travel to the beach this weekend as planned.

4. The right to vote is the **cornerstone** of a democratic society.

5. The **glib** look on the principal's face showed how proud she was of this year's graduating class.

6. The lavish party given by the CEO in an attempt to boost spirits only served to **incite** anger in the employees who did not receive bonuses.

7. Since my cousin has a photographic memory, he was able to list his extensive **pedigree** whenever prompted after studying his family tree just once.

8. The defense attorney was hopeful that evidence provided by a key witness would **exonerate** her client by verifying his alibi.

9. The **influx** of responses the reporter received after her exposé proved just how many people were interested in the subject at hand.

10. Luckily, I was able to **cleave** my assignment before the deadline and take an early vacation.

Choosing the Right Word

*Select the **boldface** word that better completes each sentence. You might refer to the passage on pages 200–201 to see how most of these words are used in context. Note that the choices might be related forms of the Unit words.*

1. Separation of powers is one of the (**cornerstones, pedigrees**) upon which the American form of government is built.

2. What we need is not talkers with (**glib, precipitous**) solutions for all our problems, but doers who are prepared to pitch in and help.

3. Modern processing methods (**devitalize, incite**) many foodstuffs sold today, resulting in a loss of both taste and nutritional value.

4. True, she comes from an aristocratic family, but she won that promotion on the basis of merit, not because of her (**pedigree, cornerstone**).

5. We are tired of listening to those (**precipitous, threadbare**) old excuses for your failure to keep your promises.

6. To seaside resorts, the annual (**influx, cornerstone**) of tourists marks the true beginning of the summer season.

7. We learned from the film that Spartacus was a Roman gladiator who (**cleaved, incited**) his fellow slaves to armed rebellion.

8. The story of his unhappy childhood aroused our sympathy but did not (**exonerate, devitalize**) him from the charge of criminal assault.

9. In a time of unrest and bewildering change, it is more important than ever to (**incite, cleave**) to the basic principles that give meaning to our lives.

10. Runaway inflation can cause a (**threadbare, precipitous**) decline in the value of a nation's currency.

11. The (**pedigree, influx**) of that dog cannot be in question; the breeder has extensive documentation to prove that he is from a line of award-winning collies.

12. With a (**precipitous, glib**) chuckle and wave of her hand, she dismissed my idea and left the room.

Completing the Sentence

Choose the word from the word bank that best completes each of the following sentences. Write the correct word or form of the word in the space provided.

| cleave | devitalize | glib | influx | precipitous |
| cornerstone | exonerate | incite | pedigree | threadbare |

1. I saw nothing but peril in the prospect of trying to scale a cliff so sheer and _____ that even expert climbers shied away from it.

2. The illness so _____ him that it was several weeks before he could return to his job.

3. The heavy rains of June brought a(n) _____ of mosquitoes into the neighborhoods bordering the marshland.

4. Her old-fashioned clothes were patched and _____, but we could see that she had made every effort to keep them spotlessly clean.

5. By proving that his eighteenth birthday came one day before the election, the student was _____ of the charge of unlawful voting.

6. The Roman numeral MCMXCVI is inscribed on the commemorative plaque that adorns the _____ of the building.

7. Rebels would find it difficult to _____ people who are reasonably well satisfied with their government to rise up against it.

8. She is certainly a(n) _____ talker, but does she have a firm grasp of the subject she is discussing?

9. With one flashing stroke of his mighty axe, the skilled woodsman was able to _____ the heavy branch from the tree trunk.

10. That dog may look like a mutt at first glance, but, in fact, it has a distinguished _____.

Synonyms

*Choose the word or form of the word from this Unit that is the same or most nearly the same in meaning as the **boldface** word or expression in the phrase. Write that word on the line. Use a dictionary if necessary.*

1. **exculpated** by last-minute eyewitness testimony _____

2. **key element** of the American Constitution _____

3. an **unpracticed** comic skit _____

4. the **addition** to the house _____

5. a **sheer** drop of 300 feet into the old quarry _____

6. an **invasion** of deer stripping the foliage _____

7. the queen's royal **lineage** _____

8. able to **sunder** a knight's shield with one blow _____

9. the **pale appearance** of a sickly child _____

10. conversation that revealed a **facile** wit _____

11. became **enfeebled** due to the hot sun _____

12. bored by the driver's **trite** jokes _____

13. pleasing design resulting from **accidental** paint drippings _____

14. the embarrassing **fiasco** of her mother's party _____

15. **entangled** in the controversy _____

Antonyms

*Choose the word or form of the word from this Unit that is most nearly opposite in meaning to the **boldface** word or expression in the phrase. Write that word on the line. Use a dictionary if necessary.*

1. **drove a wedge between** their friendship _____

2. **curb** an attack _____

3. **liberate** the prisoner _____

4. **occasional** leakage in the water pipes _____

5. his **unfriendly** tone _____

Writing: Words in Action

Choose one amazing place, construction, or invention that you would consider a wonder of the world. Write a persuasive essay explaining and supporting your choice. Support your ideas with specific examples from your studies, reading (refer to pages 200–201), or personal experience. Use three or more words from this Unit.

Vocabulary in Context

*Some of the words you have studied in this Unit appear in **boldface** type. Read the passage below, and then circle the letter of the correct answer for each word as it is used in context.*

The Wonders of the Ancient World were not chosen in any **glib, haphazard** way. They inspired amazement, awe, even disbelief. What seven structures of the last hundred years do we gaze upon and think, "Did humans really build *that*?"

Holland is mostly below sea level. That the country exists at all is a tribute to Dutch hydraulic engineering. The North Sea Protection Works is a vast, fully integrated system of dams, barriers and floodgates, estimated to be close in scale to the Great Wall of China.

Though the Empire State Building (1931) is not the tallest skyscraper in the world, the Art Deco masterpiece remains the perfect expression of the spirit of New York City.

Lt. Col. George Washington Goethals supervised the **cleaving** of a channel through the mountainous jungle terrain, and the Panama Canal opened in 1914. The canal was both a stupendous feat and a grim **debacle**; it is hard to **exonerate** Goethals from blame for the 80,000 lives lost, mostly through disease.

The stupendous Itaipu Dam crosses the Parana River at the border of Brazil and Paraguay. It is five miles wide and powers eighteen hydroelectric turbines, generating 12,000 megawatts of electricity.

The towers and spires of the Sagrada Família dominate Barcelona like a living coral forest. The **cornerstone** was laid in 1883, but Antoni Gaudí's "cathedral for the poor" will not be complete until around 2030.

The Channel Tunnel runs a distance of 31 miles at a depth of 150 feet below the English Channel to connect France and Britain. Trains 14 feet wide and two stories high run through it at 100 mph.

As it stretches across the opening of San Francisco Bay, the Golden Gate Bridge is the supreme modern example of human endeavor in harmony with nature.

---

1. The word **glib** most nearly means
   a. quick-witted
   b. affluent
   c. thoughtless
   d. wrong

2. A project that is **haphazard** is
   a. unplanned
   b. heartless
   c. careful
   d. dangerous

3. **Cleaving** a channel, as Lt. Col. Goethals did, is
   a. creating it
   b. finding it
   c. clasping it
   d. cutting it

4. An endeavor that is a **debacle** usually ends in
   a. a tie
   b. success
   c. disaster
   d. a coup

5. To **exonerate** a person from blame is to
   a. shield her
   b. forgive her
   c. absolve her
   d. incriminate her

6. The **cornerstone** of a building is the
   a. foundation
   b. starting point
   c. largest stone
   d. keystone

*Read the following passage, taking note of the **boldface** words and their contexts. These words are among those you will be studying in Unit 15. It may help you to complete the exercises in this Unit if you refer to the way the words are used below.*

Jesse Owens: 1913–1980
<Obituary>

April 1, 1980
by Mindy K. Valentine

Olympic hero Jesse Owens died yesterday in Tucson, Arizona. The cause was cancer.

Jesse Owens's story and his **legion** of achievements is compelling. The African-American track-and-field luminary captured four gold medals and set three records at the 1936 Olympics in Berlin, Germany, and his astounding achievements shattered the Nazi ideology of a so-called master race.

James Cleveland Owens was born in the segregated South, in Oakville, Alabama, in 1913. His grandparents had been enslaved, and his parents were sharecroppers who struggled to feed their children. Hoping to improve its prospects, the family resettled in Cleveland, Ohio, when J.C. was nine years old. At this time "J.C." became "Jesse"—a teacher misunderstood his strong Southern drawl when taking attendance, and the nickname stuck.

A coach in junior high recognized young Jesse's **dormant** talents and launched his track-and-field career. As a teenager, Jesse set or tied national high school records, and as a student at Ohio State University, the "Buckeye Bullet" was invincible, breaking and setting world records.

In 1936, Jesse Owens and his teammates journeyed to Berlin, Germany, to compete against the world in the Summer Olympics. Adolf Hitler was using the Games to showcase Nazi propaganda and advance his theories of racial superiority. His intentions were clear, but despite the official line, some Germans embraced Owens. One in particular, fellow Olympian Luz Long, demonstrated that not all Germans were **knaves** and villains. Owens had stepped over the start line, a fault, while trying to qualify for the finals in the long jump. This mistake **actuated** Long's helpful intervention. Following Long's advice, Owens placed a towel in front of the start line and jumped from there, keeping a safe distance from the line, and **averting** another fault and disqualification. Later, Long died a **combatant** in the German army during World War II.

Jesse Owens won four gold medals and the admiration of the world.

Legend has it that Hitler openly **spurned** Owens at the medal ceremony, but according to some historians, this part of the story is **dubious**. Owens denied that Hitler's **boorish** behavior was directed solely at him, as other African-American athletes were also present, and six of the 10 black athletes won individual gold. But news accounts said Owens bore the **brunt** of the snub, and the legend endured. Despite the achievements of Owens and his teammates, Hitler was **impenitent**; his belief in Aryan supremacy never wavered. Newsreels show him **haranguing** huge crowds about German superiority.

Owens returned home in triumph to great acclaim and a ticker-tape parade in his honor, but reality threatened to negate his achievements. In the United States, he was still a second-class citizen whom many wanted to bring down or **abase**.

Only after a **protracted** delay of several decades did he get his due. Despite setbacks, Owens was known for his grace and **liberality**, and also for his generosity to and support of young people. He started a successful national program to involve young people in track and field that enhanced his own stellar reputation.

Belatedly, Jesse Owens's own country officially recognized the significance of his achievements. He was named a Presidential Goodwill Ambassador, and he received the Medal of Freedom and Living Legend Award.

Owens is survived by his wife, Ruth, and his three daughters. His body will lie in state at the Capitol Rotunda tomorrow before his burial in Cleveland, Ohio. No further details are available.

Audio

For iWords and audio passages, go to SadlierConnect.com.

Jesse Owens and Luz Long at the Berlin Olympics

Jessie Owens traveled the country for public speaking engagements.

Definitions

Note the spelling, pronunciation, part(s) of speech, and definition(s) of each of the following words. Then write the appropriate form of the word in the blank space in the illustrative sentence(s) following.

1. abase
(ə bās')

(*v.*) to lower in esteem, degrade; to humble
My friend refused to _____ herself
by admitting to something she had not done.

2. avert
(ə vərt')

(*v.*) to turn aside, turn away; to prevent, avoid
Rigorous training of the new lifeguards will quite probably
_____ several tragedies each summer.

3. brunt
(brənt)

(*n.*) the main impact, force, or burden
Fortunately, a sparsely populated area bore the
_____ of the hurricane.

4. combatant
(kəm bat' ənt)

(*n.*) a fighter; (*adj.*) engaged in fighting
Several times the referee had to step in and separate
the two _____ after the bell rang.
The _____ forces from France and
England met on the fields near Agincourt.

5. dubious
(dü' bē əs)

(*adj.*) causing uncertainty or suspicion; in a doubtful or
uncertain state of mind, hesitant
Experts have said that the manuscript first attributed to
Mark Twain was of _____ authenticity.

6. harry
(har' ē)

(*v.*) to make a destructive raid on; to torment, harass
My parents are forever _____ me about
cleaning up my room and playing music too loudly.

7. impenitent
(im pen' ə tənt)

(*adj.*) not feeling remorse or sorrow for errors or offenses
His _____ demeanor during the trial
probably encouraged the judge to impose a harsh
sentence.

8. liberality
(lib ə ral' ə tē)

(*n.*) generosity, generous act; breadth of mind or outlook
The dean's well-known _____ allowed an
atmosphere of spirited debate to flourish at the college.

9. **probe**
(prōb)

(*v.*) to examine, investigate thoroughly; (*n.*) an investigation; a device used to explore or examine

An auditor was brought in to _____ the company's financial irregularities.

An unmanned _____ was sent to examine the geology of the Martian surface.

10. **subterfuge**
(səb′ tər fyüj)

(*n.*) an excuse or trick for escaping or hiding something

The accused embezzler's "heart attack" could be a clever _____ to avoid his upcoming trial.

Using Context

*For each item, determine whether the **boldface** word from pages 214–215 makes sense in the context of the sentence. Circle the item numbers next to the six sentences in which the words are used correctly.*

1. A helmet protects a person's head from the **brunt** of a fall or a blow.

2. You can best **abase** yourself for a test by studying over several days and then getting a good night's sleep the night before.

3. The kingdom finally reached a peace agreement with the **combatant** territories, which agreed to cease their revolt.

4. A snail's shell provides **subterfuge** for its soft, boneless body.

5. This television station always airs infomercials about "one-of-a-kind" products with **dubious** benefits or claims.

6. Many people want to work for that company because it shows great **liberality** toward its employees.

7. A hazard as simple as a slippery floor or an uneven pavement can **avert** a serious accident.

8. We watched the flock of crows in the treetops **harry** a hawk and eventually chase it away.

9. People who set **impenitent** goals for themselves are sure to meet with frustration.

10. The government will set up a committee to **probe** the corruption charges and determine whether any laws were violated.

Choosing the Right Word

*Select the **boldface** word that better completes each sentence. You might refer to the passage on pages 212–213 to see how most of these words are used in context. Note that the choices might be related forms of the Unit words.*

1. For many years after the Civil War, thousands of (**combatants, probes**) in the great battle of Gettysburg met in annual reunions.

2. Although we were fairly certain that the ice would be thick enough to hold us, we used a long stick as a (**subterfuge, probe**) to see if any part of the ice was too thin.

3. When the referee called back a touchdown by the home team, he had to bear the (**combatant, brunt**) of the crowd's anger.

4. The applicant's list of accomplishments, which went on for two pages, was (**dubious, impenitent**) at best.

5. We demand that the committee be made up of legislators who will (**abase, probe**) fearlessly into the causes of the energy crisis.

6. I was ashamed of my poor behavior at the debate and hope I did not (**harry, abase**) myself in the eyes of the moderator.

7. She pretended to be speechless with anger, but we recognized this as a (**subterfuge, liberality**) to avoid answering the charges against her.

8. Whenever I even suspect that a gory scene is about to start in a movie, I (**avert, harry**) my eyes or even cover them with my hands.

9. Since the prisoner remained defiantly (**impenitent, dubious**), the review panel saw no reason for granting him parole.

10. Your (**liberality, subterfuge**) is to be admired, but it must be controlled so that it is not out of proportion to your means.

11. A pack of reporters (**averted, harried**) the senator with pointed and persistent questions even as she was being whisked into her limousine.

12. We began with confidence in his success in the election, but as he made one mistake after another, we grew more and more (**dubious, impenitent**).

Completing the Sentence

Choose the word from the word bank that best completes each of the following sentences. Write the correct word or form of the word in the space provided.

abase	brunt	dubious	impenitent	probe
avert	combatant	harry	liberality	subterfuge

1. Why should you _____ yourself by begging to be admitted to a club made up of snobs and phonies?

2. His many donations of large sums of money to organizations dedicated to relieving world hunger are evidence of his _____.

3. The police were quickly ordered to the scene as a precautionary measure to _____ a threatened riot.

4. On the surface she seemed stubbornly _____, but secretly she regretted the damage her thoughtlessness had caused.

5. His illness was a(n) _____ to get out of taking me to the dance!

6. Divers from the salvage ship will try to _____ the ocean floor where the Confederate warship sank in 1863.

7. The two _____ fought it out with words rather than with fists.

8. Bands of guerillas _____ the straggling soldiers as they retreated in disarray.

9. Isn't friendship with a person who mistrusts you of _____ value?

10. The entire boardwalk at the beach was smashed to bits when the full _____ of the hurricane struck it.

Definitions

Note the spelling, pronunciation, part(s) of speech, and definition(s) of each of the following words. Then write the appropriate form of the word in the blank space in the illustrative sentence(s) following.

1. actuate
(ak' chü āt)

(*v.*) to move to action; to impel
A third bad accident at the notorious intersection finally
_____ an angry community protest.

2. boorish
(bùr' ish)

(*adj.*) rude, unrefined; clumsy
Her musical genius was rivaled only by her legendary
_____ behavior in public.

3. dormant
(dôr' mənt)

(*adj.*) inactive; in a state of suspension; sleeping
The warm spring sun stirred the _____
daffodil bulbs we planted in the park last fall.

4. harangue
(hə raŋ')

(*v.*) to deliver a loud, ranting speech; (*n.*) a loud speech
From the moment we walked in, our math teacher began to
_____ us about our midterm exam scores.
The speaker was supposed to discuss the criminal justice
system, but delivered a _____ against
lawyers.

5. knave
(nāv)

(*n.*) a tricky, unprincipled, or deceitful fellow
Her friends always knew that _____ of
a first husband was only after her inheritance.

6. legion
(lē' jən)

(*n.*) a large military force; any large group or number; (*adj.*)
many, numerous
It would undoubtedly take a _____ of
skilled mechanics to repair an old rattletrap like my car.
Her reasons for not attending the Community Gourmet
Club's "Cooking with Beets Night" were
_____.

7. plaintiff
(plān' tif

(*n.*) one who begins a lawsuit
His lawyers objected that the _____
rather than the defendant was being put on trial.

8. protract
(prō trakt')

(*v.*) to draw out or lengthen in space or time
Militants opposed to the peace treaty attempted
to _____ the negotiations.

9. quarry
(kwär′ ē)

(*v.*) to cut or take from (or as if from) a quarry; (*n.*) a place from which stone is taken; something that is hunted or pursued

The Internet makes it easier to _____ information from the world's vast supply.

Bargain hunters armed with sale ads raced through the store, urgently seeking their _____.

10. spurn
(spərn)

(*v.*) to refuse with scorn, disdain

He _____ a full scholarship offered by a small college to go to a big state university instead.

Using Context

*For each item, determine whether the **boldface** word from pages 218–219 makes sense in the context of the sentence. Circle the item numbers next to the six sentences in which the words are used correctly.*

1. The detectives tried for hours to **quarry** information from the witness, but he offered no details.

2. I had been worried that no one would come to my piano recital, so I was delighted to see a **legion** of friends and family in the audience.

3. I was hoping to hear more details about the candidate's platform, but his speech turned out to be nothing more than a **harangue** against his opponent.

4. I suspect that I have a **dormant** talent for painting, but I have yet to put it to the test.

5. The teachers all know my older brother as a **knave** of a student who studies diligently and always completes assignments on time.

6. The speech was interesting, but the speaker's **boorish** tone nearly put us all to sleep.

7. The editors of the newspaper decided to **actuate** the story until they had more reliable sources.

8. The **plaintiff** waited anxiously for the judge's ruling, hoping that she would win the lawsuit.

9. Although there is no cure for the common cold, drinking lots of fluids and resting can help **protract** the illness.

10. We will not be able to work together as a team if you continue to **spurn** every single one of my ideas.

Choosing the Right Word

*Select the **boldface** word that better completes each sentence. You might refer to the passage on pages 212–213 to see how most of these words are used in context. Note that the choices might be related forms of the Unit words.*

1. During the Great Depression, millions of Americans were out of work, as much of the nation's productive capacity lay (**dormant, boorish**).

2. We'll need to (**quarry, protract**) for the large stones necessary for securing the foundation.

3. After World War II, the United States and the Soviet Union became locked in a(n) (**protracted, actuated**) struggle known as the Cold War.

4. Since his absurd scheme was never really intended to harm us, we regard him as more of a fool than a (**quarry, knave**).

5. People who think only of themselves, with no concern for the feelings of others, are bound to be (**dormant, boorish**).

6. The detective story was so cleverly constructed that the character whom we took to be the pursuer turned out to be the (**quarry, plaintiff**).

7. A new popular singing idol will often (**actuate, spurn**) changes in clothing fashions.

8. The dinner to celebrate the 50th anniversary of Mrs. Roth's teaching career was attended by a (**legion, plaintiff**) of her former students.

9. In the school library, all activity seemed to have become (**dormant, legion**) as students napped with their heads and arms draped across desks.

10. At a time when we need goodwill and cooperation, nothing will be gained by an emotional (**quarry, harangue**) about old abuses and mistakes.

11. How can that heartless beauty (**harangue, spurn**) my offers of devotion!

12. I think that we can settle this dispute in a friendly way, without either of us becoming a defendant or a (**knave, plaintiff**).

Completing the Sentence

Choose the word from the word bank that best completes each of the following sentences. Write the correct word or form of the word in the space provided.

actuate	**dormant**	**knave**	**plaintiff**	**quarry**
boorish	**harangue**	**legion**	**protract**	**spurn**

1. As a lawyer for the _____, you will have full opportunity to cross-examine the witnesses for the defendant.

2. The Mississippi riverboats were home to crooks and _____ of every description, from cardsharps to confidence men.

3. The sudden and violent eruption of a volcano that had been _____ for many years destroyed Pompeii in two days.

4. The soldiers of the mighty Roman _____ were organized in battle units called cohorts and maniples.

5. The "Speakers' Corner" in London's Hyde Park is home to soapbox orators who _____ idlers and passersby.

6. Fortunately, the loud and generally _____ behavior of a few of the guests did not spoil the party for the rest of us.

7. Our planned stopover in Denver was unexpectedly _____ when a blizzard prevented us from leaving the city for days.

8. Because her feelings were hurt, she _____ any attempts on my part to provide help.

9. The bloodhounds pursued their human _____ through the swamps.

10. We learned that the bizarre sequence of events was _____ by an accidental tug on the switching device.

Synonyms

*Choose the word or form of the word from this Unit that is the same or most nearly the same in meaning as the **boldface** word or expression in the phrase. Write that word on the line. Use a dictionary if necessary.*

1. a display of **unrepentant** behavior at the hearing   _____

2. investigators who will **scrutinize** their files   _____

3. an arts foundation famous for its **largesse**   _____

4. the testimony of the **accuser**   _____

5. tried to **pester** her mother into changing her mind   _____

6. escape by means of a **ruse** involving false noses   _____

7. a **soldier** preparing for battle   _____

8. a new contract that **precluded** a labor dispute   _____

9. a **tirade** prompted by a messy room   _____

10. felt the **impact** of the crash   _____

11. an attempt to **trigger** impeachment proceedings   _____

12. mined limestone from a large **pit** near the site   _____

13. fooled by that **rascal**   _____

14. a conflict **extended** by cease-fire violations   _____

15. lies **asleep** in a cocoon   _____

Antonyms

*Choose the word or form of the word from this Unit that is most nearly opposite in meaning to the **boldface** word or expression in the phrase. Write that word on the line. Use a dictionary if necessary.*

1. **elevated** themselves in the eyes of the judge   _____

2. **sophisticated** manners   _____

3. **welcomed** his offer to help   _____

4. a **small number** of supporters   _____

5. cited a **reliable** narrative   _____

Writing: Words in Action

Is a hero someone who shows courage, who is exceptionally talented at something, or who accomplishes something great? In a brief essay, present your definition of a hero, and use examples from your observations, studies, reading (refer to pages 212–213), or personal experience. Use three or more words from this Unit.

Vocabulary in Context

*Some of the words you have studied in this Unit appear in **boldface** type. Read the passage below, and then circle the letter of the correct answer for each word as it is used in context.*

When Rio de Janeiro was awarded the 2016 Olympics, Brazil's economy was strong and its leaders confident. Not long afterward, the price of oil plunged, and with it the Brazilian economy, which depended heavily on oil revenues. Budget shortfalls undermined state and national governments. Shortly before the Games began, the governor of Rio declared a "financial disaster," raising concerns about security. There was no money to fill police cars with gasoline, and police officials had to ask for donations of cleaning supplies and toilet paper. Crime victims and **plaintiffs**, their cases languishing for lack of printer paper, were forced to **harry** unfortunate court workers to have their cases brought to trial.

Brazil's financial woes also affected preparations for the Games. Twelve million people live in Rio's metropolitan area, and much of the city's sewage flows untreated into Guanabara Bay, where sailors, marathon swimmers, and triathletes would compete. Eight new wastewater treatment plants had been promised, but the government could only afford to build one. Scientists began to **probe** the polluted waters for microscopic **quarry**—water-borne bacteria and viruses. The results were alarming. Virus levels, for example, were 1.7 million times what would be considered dangerous along California's beaches. The city did step up its efforts to clean floating trash from the bay, but many observers considered the initiative a **subterfuge**, since it ignored the invisible but more serious microbial threat.

Not all of Rio's pre-Olympic headaches were self-inflicted. Transmitted by **legions** of tropical mosquitoes, the Zika virus was inadvertently introduced to the region several years before the Games. Fortunately, scientists at the World Health Organization determined that Zika posed little danger to fans or athletes. The Games could go on.

---

1. The word **harry** most nearly means
  a. harass   **c.** plead
  b. humiliate   **d.** abuse

2. Plaintiffs start
  a. petitions   **c.** campaigns
  b. lawsuits   **d.** investigations

3. To **probe** a bay's waters, scientists
  a. dive into it   **c.** research it
  b. disinfect it   **d.** examine it

4. A **quarry** is something that is being
  a. cornered   **c.** eliminated
  b. pursued   **d.** pictured

5. An action is a **subterfuge** if it
  a. is popular   **c.** hides something
  b. is hidden   **d.** reveals a truth

6. If there are **legions** of mosquitoes, there are
  a. many   **c.** control experts
  b. some   **d.** diseases

Vocabulary for Comprehension
Part 1

*Read this passage, which contains words in **boldface** that appear in Units 13–15. Then choose the best answer to each question based on what is stated or implied in the passage. You may refer to the passage as often as necessary.*

Questions 1–10 are based on the following passage.

In literature, important people or notable events have influenced the lives of some writers. One specific writer, Henry David Thoreau, was so influenced by nature that
(5) it led to his masterpiece: *Walden*. Several significant literary movements have been shaped by place and time, including the Bloomsbury group, the Lost Generation, and the Harlem Renaissance.

(10)   The Bloomsbury group was a name of a group of English writers, philosophers, and artists who met from 1907 to 1930 in the Bloomsbury district of London. The area had elegant townhouses that circled
(15) an open garden space. The backdrop of the museum and this picturesque district shaped the group's ideas about beauty: Its members tried to define the good, the true, and the beautiful, and they wanted to
(20) **sever** themselves from the constraints of the **boorish** previous generation. This aestheticism, coupled with philosophy, provided the **cornerstone** for the group's beliefs. The Bloomsbury group also
(25) shared their work with one another and supported each other's creative endeavors. Virginia Woolf and E.M. Forster were two well-known members of the Bloomsbury group.

(30)   While the Bloomsbury group was defined by place, the Lost Generation was defined by a tumultuous time in American history. The Lost Generation was a name given to a group of writers who grew up
(35) during World War I and established themselves professionally during the 1920s. As **legions** of soldiers left the battlefields and returned to the United States after the war ended in 1918, the
(40) Lost Generation grew **dubious** about the ideals of the world. Thus, the generation was called "lost" because the ideas that they had grown up with were **untenable** in the postwar world. Although all of the Lost
(45) Generation writers were American, many members emigrated to Europe after the war. The most famous Lost Generation writers were Ernest Hemingway, Gertrude Stein, F. Scott Fitzgerald, and T.S. Eliot.

(50)   The Harlem Renaissance was a period defined by a boom in African American artistic and creative expression. Many readers were fascinated by Harlem; thus, the publishing industry reached out to
(55) African American writers to realistically depict black life there. From 1917 to 1935, the thriving cultural metropolis of Harlem beckoned artists, writers, and poets to this northern hub of New York City, where they
(60) could express themselves freely. Many of the arrivals to Harlem came from the South during the Great **Migration**: a time when millions of African American Southerners left the South and moved to
(65) other parts of the country. This **influx** of African Americans into the North increased the population of Harlem, thus increasing its creative output. In Harlem, these newcomers hoped to find a place
(70) where they could create art and live away from the problems in which they had been **embroiled**. Writers like Langston Hughes, Jean Toomer, and Zora Neale Hurston wrote realistic stories and poems about
(75) black life, and Harlem influenced the subject matter of many other works.

1. The main idea of this passage is that
A) many writers were so influenced by *Walden* that they wrote about nature.
B) some famous literary movements have been inspired by place and time.
C) free expression defined the Bloomsbury group and the Harlem Renaissance.
D) all famous writers were part of significant literary movements.

2. As it is used in line 20, "sever" most nearly means
A) separate.
B) distinguish.
C) alter.
D) hide.

3. How did the Bloomsbury district influence the writers of the Bloomsbury group?
A) The gardens of the Bloomsbury district caused them to write about nature.
B) The proximity to the British Museum caused them to think about famous artists.
C) The setting of greater London made them think about deeper philosophical ideas.
D) The beauty of the Bloomsbury district made them think about aesthetics.

4. The Lost Generation writers were "lost"
A) because they felt lost in Europe after leaving the United States.
B) because they got lost in their literary lives while living in Europe.
C) because they were part of a small group of American Writers in Europe.
D) because after World War I, they felt disillusioned about society's values.

5. As it is used in line 37, the word "legion" most nearly means
A) a large military force.
B) a fleet of naval ships.
C) a group of immigrants.
D) a small number of people.

6. The Great Migration influenced the Harlem Renaissance by
A) influencing Southern ideas about nature.
B) bringing Southerners to Harlem where they could express their creativity.
C) allowing writers to focus on the problems they left behind in the South.
D) publishing African American writers.

7. Which choice provides the best evidence for the answer to the previous question?
A) Lines 52–53 ("Many . . . Harlem")
B) Lines 56–60 ("From 1917, . . . freely")
C) Lines 60–65 ("Many . . . country")
D) Lines 65–68 ("This influx . . . output")

8. As it is used in line 65, the word "influx" most nearly means
A) change.
B) output.
C) inflow.
D) decrease.

9. Which of the following statements is supported by the passage?
A) Many Lost Generation writers lived in Europe, but the other movements were based in the United States.
B) The Lost Generation writers focused more on a specific time in history, while the other movements developed around a specific place.
C) The Lost Generation was an artistic and literary movement, while the other movements were literary.
D) The Lost Generation writers were the only ones who experienced the aftermath of World War I.

10. It can reasonably be inferred that the author believes that
A) some literary movements were more influential than others.
B) each respective movement was important for those involved in it.
C) literary movements provided important inspiration for a variety of creative work.
D) literary movements were very popular during their respective time frames.

Vocabulary for Comprehension
Part 2

*Read this passage, which contain words in **boldface** that appear in Units 13–15. Then choose the best answer to each question based on what is stated or implied in the passage. You may refer to the passage as often as necessary.*

Questions 1–10 are based on the following passage.

One of the most important writers to emerge from the Harlem Renaissance was Langston Hughes. The story of his prodigious talent preceded his birth: his
(5) maternal great uncle, John Mercer Langston, was appointed as Minister to Haiti. Charles Henry, Hughes's maternal grandfather, represented Virginia in the U.S. Congress. His maternal grandmother,
(10) Mary Patterson Leary, was among the first to attend Oberlin College, and her first husband, Lewis Sheridan Leary, participated in John Brown's abolitionist raid of Harper's Ferry. This notable
(15) **pedigree** provided Hughes with his determination and work ethic.

Hughes was born in Joplin, Missouri, in 1902 and raised by his maternal grandmother until his early teens. After his
(20) grandmother's death, he moved in with his mother and her husband, and the family lived in several Midwestern cities before settling in Cleveland, Ohio. Ethel Weimer, Hughes's tenth-grade English teacher at
(25) Central High School in Cleveland, introduced him to Carl Sandburg and Walt Whitman. Hughes **probed** their works, ultimately leading him to write his own poetry; while living in a third-floor **annex** of
(30) a house in Cleveland, Hughes continued to write. Shortly after graduating from high school, Hughes published his first poem in the magazine *The Crisis*. In 1921, Hughes was briefly enrolled in Columbia
(35) University and became acquainted with the Harlem Renaissance while living in New York City. He quickly became a part of this movement and befriended an elite **clique** of Harlem Renaissance writers,
(40) including W.E.B. DuBois, James Weldon Johnson, Alain Locke, Countee Cullen, and Zora Neale Hurston.

In 1925, Hughes's poem "The Weary Blues" won first prize in the *Opportunity*
(45) magazine literary competition, and Hughes received a scholarship to attend Lincoln University. At Lincoln, Hughes met novelist and critic Carl Van Vechten, who helped publish Hughes's first book
(50) of poetry, *The Weary Blues*, in 1926. One year later, Hughes published a second book of poetry. After graduating from Lincoln University, Hughes achieved a **lofty** goal: he published his first novel,
(55) *Not Without Laughter*. The money from this commercially successful publication allowed Hughes to make his living as a writer. In the late 1930s, Hughes's **liberality** with artistic ideas beyond poetry
(60) and prose led him to form several theater companies in Chicago, New York, and Los Angeles. In 1951, Hughes was **actuated** by the desperation that he **perceived** within northern African American
(65) communities, and it inspired his poem *Montage of a Dream Deferred*. Around this time, Hughes was increasingly hounded about his connections to communism. In 1953, he testified in front of Senator
(70) Eugene McCarthy's Committee on Un-American Activities. His reputation was somewhat tarnished during this period, though he renounced all ties to communism. He was never formally
(75) charged, and was subsequently **exonerated** in the public's opinion as McCarthy's mission was discredited.

Hughes continued writing until his death in 1967; ultimately, he wrote eleven plays
(80) and numerous poems and prose works. His ashes are buried in the Harlem that he loved, beneath the entrance of the Schomburg Center for Black Culture. The inscription marking the spot says
(85) "My soul has grown deep like the rivers," which is a famous line from his first poem.

1. What point is the author making by including the first paragraph?
A) Langston Hughes had a large family.
B) Hughes's ancestors helped him.
C) Hughes's success does not compare to that of his family.
D) Hughes was influenced by his successful lineage.

2. As it is used in line 15, "pedigree" most nearly means
A) list of ancestors.
B) list of characteristics.
C) list of occupations.
D) list of locations.

3. Which life experience directly impacted Hughes's decision to write poetry?
A) living with his grandmother as a child
B) moving to several Midwestern cities as a teenager
C) being exposed to poets in high school
D) attending Columbia University

4. As it is used in line 27, "probe" most nearly means
A) examine.
B) seek.
C) define.
D) clarify.

5. The author uses lines 66–74 in this passage to show
A) that Hughes's life was controversial.
B) an obstacle that Hughes overcame.
C) that Hughes's career never fully recovered after this occasion.
D) the ways that Hughes's reputation was tarnished by this committee.

6. Hughes was most interested in
A) producing highly regarded poetry.
B) cultivating his diverse artistic interests.
C) becoming commercially successful.
D) being part of the Harlem Renaissance.

7. Which choice provides the best evidence for the answer to the previous question?
A) Lines 23–31 ("Ethel . . . write")
B) Lines 37–42 ("He quickly . . . Hurston")
C) Lines 52–58 ("After . . . writer")
D) Lines 58–62 ("In . . . Los Angeles")

8. As it is used in line 63, "perceive" most nearly means
A) compare.
B) observe.
C) discuss.
D) extinguish.

9. It can reasonably be inferred that a line from Hughes's first poem is included to
A) provide evidence for why Hughes was buried in Harlem.
B) illustrate the powerful message that Hughes's poem contains.
C) show how one line of the poem captured Hughes's life.
D) highlight why it was the most famous line Hughes had written.

10. The main idea of the passage is that
A) Langston Hughes's life influenced other poets and writers of the Harlem Renaissance.
B) Langston Hughes wrote about the life experiences of African Americans in Harlem.
C) Langston Hughes produced a wealth of work that influenced American literature.
D) Langston Hughes was the most important writer to emerge from the Harlem Renaissance.

Synonyms

*From the word bank below, choose the word that has the same or nearly the same meaning as the **boldface** word in each sentence and write it on the line. You will not use all of the words.*

abase	combatant	influx	precipitous
actuate	devitalize	knave	quarry
ad infinitum	exonerate	perceive	rancid
boorish	impenitent	plaintiff	vindicate

1. The **complainant** is currently considering a settlement offer that was made by the defendant's lawyer. _____

2. Chicken salad must be either refrigerated or eaten right away because it can become **rotten** quickly. _____

3. You have always been an honest and kind person, and I know you would not **lower** yourself through lies and name-calling. _____

4. The population of the seaside town triples every summer because of the **inpouring** of tourists and part-time residents. _____

5. Loyal fans hoped that their beloved team would **justify** their dedication by breaking a thirty-year losing streak. _____

6. I could go on **forever** about why *Moby-Dick* is such a great novel, but instead you should just try reading it yourself. _____

7. The twins are sometimes overactive and **ill-mannered**, but today they were on their best behavior. _____

8. Anamorphosis is a technique for drawing images that viewers will **observe** as being three-dimensional. _____

9. In the science fiction movie, explorers of deep space become the **prey** of a terrifying assortment of alien predators. _____

10. Riders in the Tour de France bike race excel at handling many conditions, from flat roads, to rolling hills, to **steep** mountain climbs. _____

11. What kind of **rogue** would steal a bench from a public park? _____

12. The defense lawyer claimed that video evidence showing her client in another town at the time of the crime would **clear** the suspect. _____

Two-Word Completions

Select the pair of words that best completes the meaning of each of the following sentences.

1. Over the years, the _____ of our patrons and sponsors has kept the wolf from our door more than once. Without their generous support, I honestly don't know how our little theater company would have _____ disaster.
   a. liberality . . . averted
   b. migration . . . shackled
   c. clique . . . reconciled
   d. versatility . . . spurned

2. "You'll usually win a debate if your arguments are valid and convincing," I observed. "But if your position is _____, you'll eventually be forced to _____ defeat."
   a. glib . . . improvise
   b. bona fide . . . avert
   c. dubious . . . spurn
   d. untenable . . . concede

3. Most dictators don't just address their audiences; they _____ them. Their words are not meant to soothe or enlighten; they are designed to _____ the listener to violence and hatred.
   a. probe . . . harry
   b. harangue . . . incite
   c. improvise . . . embroil
   d. apportion . . . reconcile

4. We can go ahead with this project just as soon as we know we have the money to finance it in the bank. Unfortunately, the plan must remain _____ as long as the necessary financial resources are _____.
   a. sordid . . . haphazard
   b. bona fide . . . perverse
   c. dormant . . . dubious
   d. untenable . . . profuse

5. Before the curtain goes up on the first act, the orchestra plays a short _____ depicting in musical terms the _____ ideals of the high-minded knight who is the hero of the opera.
   a. pedigree . . . threadbare
   b. brunt . . . glib
   c. prelude . . . lofty
   d. debacle . . . buoyant

6. Though urban life may suit some people to a tee, I have always found a _____ environment more _____.
   a. cordial . . . haphazard
   b. rustic . . . congenial
   c. lofty . . . protracted
   d. sordid . . . perverse

7. As Great Britain's power and prestige began to _____ and lose their luster, subjects all over the empire rose up to demand release from the onerous _____ that bound them so firmly to the motherland.
   a. pall . . . cornerstones
   b. cleave . . . subterfuges
   c. concede . . . cliques
   d. wane . . . shackles

Idioms

In the passage "Jesse Owens: 1913–1980" (see pages 212–213), the author says that Owens "bore the brunt of the snub."

"Bore the brunt of the snub" is an idiom that means "to receive the worst part of something unpleasant." An **idiom** is a common saying, an informal expression that conveys its meaning in nonliteral terms. A reader cannot usually "decode" an idiom by looking at the meaning of each of the words that form it. To understand the meaning of an idiom, readers often have to simply learn what it means, similar to learning the meaning of a new vocabulary word.

Choosing the Right Idiom

*Read each sentence. Use context clues to figure out the meaning of each idiom in **boldface**. Then write the letter of the definition for the idiom in the sentence.*

1. We need to **strike a balance** between the opposing parties. _____

2. I will be the **devil's advocate** and suggest that the reason you didn't get the job is that the manager didn't like you. _____

3. Do not **shoot yourself in the foot** by dressing sloppily on the day of your big interview. _____

4. To find a solution to this unusual problem, we have to **think outside the box**. _____

5. The prodigy could play Mozart **by ear**. _____

6. I am almost done—don't **breathe down my neck**! _____

7. When it is my turn to plan a party, I will **call the shots** and choose the music myself. _____

8. When I asked why she was late, that really opened up a **can of worms**. _____

9. If no one wants this last orange, I guess it is **fair game**. _____

10. She was **hands down** the most talented singer in the contest. _____

a. go beyond traditional ideas

b. make things more equal

c. after listening to something, and without a written guide

d. someone who states the less popular viewpoint for the sake of argument

e. be in charge; direct the action

f. monitor someone closely in an unpleasant way

g. something that is troublesome and problematic

h. undermine yourself

i. without a doubt

j. available to anyone who wants

Classical Roots

vert, vers—to turn

This root appears in **versatile** (page 191). The literal meaning of this word is "able to be turned." In modern usage it now refers to the ability to turn from one task to another with ease. Some other words based on the same root are listed below.

adversity	conversion	divert	reversion
aversion	diversion	invert	version

From the list of words above, choose the one that corresponds to each of the brief definitions below. Write the word in the blank space in the illustrative sentence below the definition. Use an online or print dictionary if necessary.

1. distress, misfortune, hardship

It is said that _____ can make victory sweeter.

2. to turn aside; to entertain, amuse

A magician's most important task is to _____ the attention of an audience from the sleight of hand that makes the trick work.

3. a change in condition or belief (*"turning toward"*)

The physical _____ of solid ice into liquid water is known as melting.

4. a return to a former state, belief, or condition; a reversal

After some false starts, the coach made a(n) _____ to a more traditional practice routine.

5. a particular form of something; an account of an incident

After much gossip and speculation, we were eager to hear the official _____ of the story.

6. a turning aside; any distraction of attention; amusement, entertainment; pastime

Many students find athletics to be an excellent _____ from the academic pressures of school.

7. to turn upside down; to change direction

The trick required them to _____ a glass of water without spilling any of its contents.

8. a strong dislike; a thing disliked (*"turning against"*)

I'm not really sure why I've developed such a strong _____ to country music.

Synonyms

Select the two words or expressions that are most nearly the same in meaning.

1. **a.** recoil　　**b.** scream　　**c.** draw back　　**d.** adjourn
2. **a.** educate　　**b.** cling　　**c.** hew　　**d.** hamper
3. **a.** preamble　　**b.** semblance　　**c.** adherent　　**d.** introduction
4. **a.** arrival　　**b.** opposition　　**c.** expulsion　　**d.** advent
5. **a.** alert　　**b.** sweet　　**c.** candid　　**d.** outspoken
6. **a.** improve　　**b.** begin　　**c.** institute　　**d.** end
7. **a.** quaver　　**b.** comport　　**c.** protest　　**d.** behave
8. **a.** rustic　　**b.** rough　　**c.** pliant　　**d.** rugged
9. **a.** confused　　**b.** rancid　　**c.** arbitrary　　**d.** garbled
10. **a.** opponent　　**b.** plaintiff　　**c.** supporter　　**d.** proponent
11. **a.** skilled　　**b.** awkward　　**c.** adept　　**d.** concerted
12. **a.** sincere　　**b.** plentiful　　**c.** profuse　　**d.** scarce
13. **a.** sever　　**b.** venture　　**c.** escalate　　**d.** increase
14. **a.** annihilate　　**b.** torture　　**c.** destroy　　**d.** build up
15. **a.** brevity　　**b.** prelude　　**c.** liability　　**d.** conciseness

Antonyms

Select the two words or expressions that are most nearly opposite in meaning.

16. **a.** bona fide　　**b.** versatile　　**c.** erratic　　**d.** bogus
17. **a.** abased　　**b.** alien　　**c.** lofty　　**d.** glib
18. **a.** actuate　　**b.** terminate　　**c.** commandeer　　**d.** hoodwink
19. **a.** usurp　　**b.** surmount　　**c.** succumb　　**d.** annex
20. **a.** incite　　**b.** devitalize　　**c.** apportion　　**d.** rejuvenate
21. **a.** illustrious　　**b.** haphazard　　**c.** circumspect　　**d.** languid
22. **a.** comely　　**b.** tenacious　　**c.** cumbersome　　**d.** repugnant
23. **a.** fortify　　**b.** tantalize　　**c.** emancipate　　**d.** shackle
24. **a.** defray　　**b.** abscond　　**c.** disentangle　　**d.** embroil
25. **a.** lithe　　**b.** militant　　**c.** lucid　　**d.** opaque

Two-Word Completions

Select the pair of words that best completes the meaning of each of the following sentences.

26. Although Scott inherited a great deal of money, he lived as a(n) _____ and never _____ a cent.

    a. envoy . . . relinquished   **c.** vagrant . . . condoned

    b. pauper . . . squandered   **d.** accomplice . . . impoverished

27. Though she gained fame _____, nobody thought she was an _____ artist while she was alive.

    a. illegibly . . . sprightly   **c.** incorrigibly . . . lucrative

    b. superfluously . . . intrepid   **d.** posthumously . . . eminent

28. My dog, Lucky, is small, but he has a(n) _____ attitude and gets into scuffles that he could have easily _____.

    a. cherubic . . . forestalled   **c.** pugnacious . . . averted

    b. preposterous . . . facilitated   **d.** boorish . . . actuated

29. The child was engaged in an animated _____, describing to her stuffed toys the _____ over which she was queen.

    a. monologue . . . realm   **c.** prototype . . . gluttony

    b. catalyst . . . exodus   **d.** altercation . . . rift

30. The boy ran with _____ happiness for an afternoon of fishing at the _____.

    a. momentous . . . muddle   **c.** surly . . . tirade

    b. obtrusive . . . quarry   **d.** unbridled . . . rivulet

31. Anne's face took on an unnatural _____ when she realized she could not get out of the _____.

    a. deadlock . . . clique   **c.** pallor . . . dilemma

    b. larceny . . . debacle   **d.** prognosis . . . migration

32. The mechanic was _____ about his ability to keep a vehicle of such _____ quality on the road.

    a. slapdash . . . sparse   **c.** opinionated . . . morose

    b. skeptical . . . shoddy   **d.** perilous . . . prim

Supplying Words in Context

To complete each sentence, select the best word from among the choices given. Not all words in the word bank will be used. You may modify the word form as necessary.

abridge	immunity	pilfer	taunt
depreciation	impair	recoup	terse
exorcise	malign	sardonic	untenable
fodder	pensive	stagnant	wily

33. The suspect agreed to testify against the other conspirators in exchange for _____ from prosecution.

34. All that we heard from my mysterious aunt was the _____ message "I have arrived."

35. Lack of practice will certainly _____ your tennis game.

36. As he presented his explanation of the causes of inflation, his position seemed to me weak and _____.

37. One who begins by _____ pennies may end by stealing millions.

38. Her job for the next year was to _____ the two-volume biography into a single book.

access	bleak	impel	predispose
alien	debris	interim	staccato
apex	despicable	intricate	trite
assimilate	flippant	obstreperous	wane

39. We felt rather gloomy as we looked out on the _____ winter scene under the weak light of the moon.

40. His _____ wisecracks were clever but in bad taste.

41. In the _____ between the two semesters, we will enjoy a brief vacation at the seashore.

42. Do you realize how _____ a job it is to reschedule so many programs on the spur of the moment?

43. Scattered all over the beach was _____ from the wrecked ship.

44. As night came on and it became much colder, the courage of the runaways _____.

Word Associations

*Select the word or expression that best completes the meaning of the sentence or answers the question, with particular reference to the meaning of the word in **boldface** type.*

45. You might say **adieu**
    a. when you arrive
    b. when you leave
    c. when someone sneezes
    d. when you step on someone's toes

46. The word **horde** might be used to describe
    a. an individual working alone
    b. an invading army
    c. a symphony orchestra
    d. an efficient group of workers

47. An **invincible** team is one that has never known
    a. the fear of flying
    b. injury or illness
    c. the joy of victory
    d. the agony of defeat

48. We may apply the word **dormant** to
    a. shackles and freedom
    b. the moon and the stars
    c. a talent and a volcano
    d. a poem and a song

49. Which nickname would a **doleful** person be most likely to have?
    a. Little Mo
    b. Broadway Joe
    c. Sad Sam
    d. Big John

50. Which of the following might apply to a person who is **mediocre**?
    a. immortal
    b. illustrious
    c. sterling
    d. undistinguished

51. A mistake that is **grievous** is
    a. serious
    b. widespread
    c. unnoticed
    d. simple

52. A country in a state of **anarchy** does NOT have
    a. law and order
    b. arts and sciences
    c. food and water
    d. education and medicine

53. A word closely associated with **altercation** is
    a. adherent
    b. revision
    c. argument
    d. sensible

54. A person who seeks **asylum** is looking for
    a. protection
    b. public office
    c. an easy job
    d. an orphan to adopt

55. We can apply the word **meander** to
    a. sellers and buyers
    b. plaintiffs and defendants
    c. rivers and arguments
    d. victories and defeats

56. Which description would NOT apply to a typical **metropolis**?
    a. crowded
    b. bustling
    c. rustic
    d. large

Choosing the Right Meaning

Read each sentence carefully. Then select the item that best completes the statement below the sentence.

57. Although the price we paid for the tickets seemed **exorbitant**, the experience of seeing the musicians in a live performance was well worth the money.

In line 1 the word **exorbitant** most nearly means

a. reasonable   **b.** unproven   **c.** modest   **d.** excessive

58. During the heat wave, power was **erratic** and the electricity frequently went out for 15 minutes or more.

The word **erratic** in line 1 most nearly means

a. expensive   **b.** strong   **c.** unbearable   **d.** undependable

59. Security officers never found out how the thieves were able to **access** the vaults in the basement of the bank.

The best definition for the word **access** in line 1 is

a. locate   **b.** approach   **c.** gain entry to   **d.** visualize

60. The computer **console** was so small that I strained my eyes using it.

In line 1 the word **console** most nearly means

a. comfort   **b.** monitor   **c.** cost   **d.** keyboard

61. My grandmother gave me a set of antique **cordial** glasses that had been in the family for generations.

In line 1 the word **cordial** most nearly means

a. water   **b.** friendship   **c.** crystal   **d.** liqueur

62. At the end of the long, hard trip out West, the pioneers appeared as only a **semblance** of their former selves.

In line 1 the word **semblance** most nearly means

a. likeness   **b.** enemy   **c.** fraction   **d.** relative

63. The woman's flashy car, designer clothes, elaborate hairdo, and entourage of newly acquired friends **reeked** of a recent windfall.

The word **reeked** in line 2 most nearly means

a. gave the impression   **c.** was invulnerable to
b. was the opposite   **d.** smelled unpleasant

64. The young potatoes must be **blanched** before they are roasted in the oven.

In line 1 the word **blanched** is best defined as

a. discolored   **b.** mashed   **c.** boiled briefly   **d.** seasoned

65. When I was a child, my worried mother frequently **admonished** me against riding my bike without a helmet.

The word **admonished** in line 1 most nearly means

a. cautioned   **b.** prevented   **c.** rewarded   **d.** reminded

The following is a list of all the words taught in the Units of this book. The number after each entry indicates the page on which the word is defined.

abase, 214
abridge, 38
abscond, 62
access, 62
accomplice, 74
actuate, 218
ad infinitum, 194
adept, 146
adherent, 42
adieu, 102
adjourn, 30
admonish, 14
advent, 102
alien, 26
altercation, 38
anarchy, 58
annex, 202
annihilate, 74
apex, 106
apportion, 190
appreciable, 174
arbitrary, 70
arduous, 62
aspire, 150
assimilate, 106
assurance, 118
asylum, 114
atone, 82
auspicious, 58
autocratic, 170
auxiliary, 130
avert, 214

blanch, 174
blasphemy, 170
bleak, 150
bogus, 106
bona fide, 194
bondage, 86

boorish, 218
brawny, 174
brazen, 74
breach, 18
brevity, 158
brigand, 14
brunt, 214
buoyant, 190

candid, 130
catalyst, 70
cherubic, 42
chide, 146
circumspect, 18
cleave, 206
clique, 190
combatant, 214
comely, 26
commandeer, 14
compensate, 30
comport, 162
concede, 194
concerted, 170
concise, 158
condone, 42
congenial, 190
console, 114
contend, 174
cordial, 202
cornerstone, 206
credible, 82
cubicle, 126
cumbersome, 14

daunt, 58
deadlock, 18
debacle, 202
debris, 18
defray, 86

demure, 162
depreciation, 162
despicable, 146
deteriorate, 158
devitalize, 206
diffuse, 14
dilate, 118
dilemma, 14
diligent, 86
diminutive, 150
disentangle, 62
dissent, 38
dissolute, 30
divulge, 162
doleful, 82
dormant, 218
dross, 118
drudgery, 126
dubious, 214
dwindle, 114

efface, 18
emancipate, 150
embroil, 202
eminent, 38
enlightened, 158
envoy, 130
erratic, 26
erroneous, 146
escalate, 126
exodus, 74
exonerate, 206
exorbitant, 102
exorcise, 42
expedient, 126
exploit, 146
expulsion, 30
extemporaneous, 150

fabricate, 38
facilitate, 70
fated, 62
feign, 130
feint, 30
flair, 130
flippant, 114
fodder, 26
forestall, 158
fortify, 26

garble, 162
ghastly, 86
glib, 206
gluttony, 42
grievous, 126

hamper, 82
haphazard, 202
harangue, 218
harry, 214
heterogeneous, 130
hew, 86
hoodwink, 58
horde, 126
humane, 174

illegible, 30
illustrious, 174
immunity, 118
impair, 146
impel, 126
impenitent, 214
impoverished, 82
improvise, 202
inanimate, 58
incessant, 86
incinerate, 58
incite, 206

WORD LIST

SCHOLASTIC FIRST DISCOVERY

The Rain Forest

Created by Gallimard Jeunesse
and René Mettler
Illustrated by René Mettler

SCHOLASTIC REFERENCE
an imprint of
SCHOLASTIC

If you flew over the world's largest rain forest, you would see an endless canopy of tall green trees. This steamy forest is called the Amazon. It covers a third of South America.

The muddy Amazon River winds through the warm, rainy forest for 4,000 miles.

Deep in the rain
forest, tropical plants
grow so close
together that
you need a
machete to cut
a path through
them.

If you flew over the world's largest rain forest, you would see an endless canopy of tall green trees. This steamy forest is called the Amazon. It covers a third of South America.

The muddy Amazon River winds through the warm, rainy forest for 4,000 miles.

Deep in the rain
forest, tropical plants
grow so close
together that
you need a
machete to cut
a path through
them.

Many animals live in the rain forest. How many can you find in this picture?

Amazing plants also grow in the rain forest. Water lily leaves float on water. They may be as big as rugs.

Some plants provide fruits, nuts, and ingredients for many of our medicines.

Air plants grow on branches. They do not need soil.

Some flowers grow on tree trunks.

Others bloom at the ends of long, hanging stems.

Very tall trees grow side supports called buttresses, which help them stand up.

Monkeys also live in the rain forest. They climb and swing from tree to tree.

Some monkeys, like the sapajou, are small.

Others, like the noisy howler monkey, are big.

Fabulous birds live
in the rain forest.
The smallest of all
is the hummingbird.
It drinks nectar
from brightly
colored flowers.

It uses its long
beak and tongue
to reach the
nectar.

Slaty-headed parakeet

Sun parakeet

Amazon parakeet with cheeks

All kinds of parakeets
live in the rain forest.

Monk
parakeet

Yellow-fronted
parakeet

Amazon parakeet with
yellow forehead

Lucien parakeet

This large bird is called a toucan (rhymes with "you can"). It has a big, colorful bill. There are different kinds of toucans.

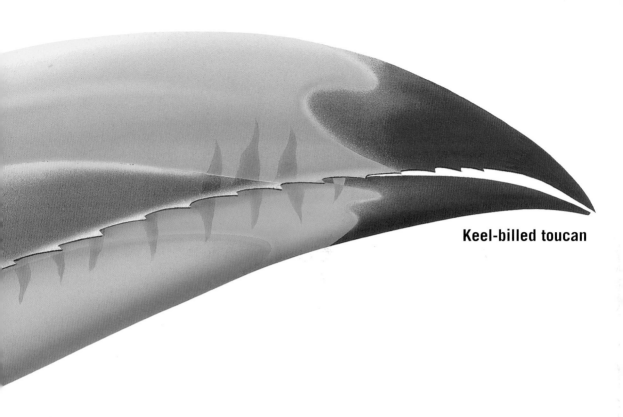

Keel-billed toucan

Toco toucan

Red-topped toucan

Aracari toucan

These capuchin monkeys
sense that danger is near.
What could it be?

A jaguar
on the hunt!

The tapir does not hear
the jaguar coming.
It may become a meal
for the big cat.

These rain forest animals are as brightly colored as a rainbow.

Red vakari

Red ibis

The dentrobate tree frog is pretty— but poisonous!

Coral serpent

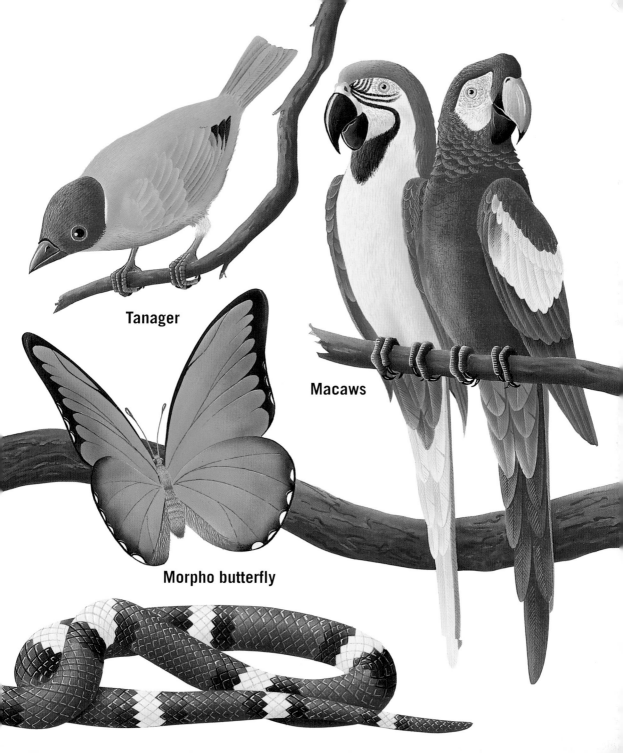

Tanager

Macaws

Morpho butterfly

Can you find
three insects
hidden here?

Camouflaged animals
have colors and shapes
that help them hide
from animals that feed
on them.

The two grasshoppers
look like green leaves.
The brown moth looks
like a dead leaf.

The Amazon rain forest—
home to so many beautiful
animals and valuable plants—
is being attacked by an enemy.
Who is it?

People!

People have cut down trees for lumber or
burned acres of rain forest for farmland.
Thankfully, other people are working to find
ways of harvesting the Amazon's natural
resources without destroying it.